GREAT EXPERIMENTERS

great
EXPERIMENTERS

by WILLIAM BIXBY

David McKay Company Inc.
New York

GREAT EXPERIMENTERS

FIRST EDITION SEPTEMBER 1964
REPRINTED AUGUST 1966

LIBRARY OF CONGRESS CATALOG CARD NUMBER: 64–19408

MANUFACTURED IN THE UNITED STATES OF AMERICA

Contents

Preface

One of the most disturbing trends in today's world is the tendency of many people to worship science. Scientists and nonscientists alike frequently write and talk and think of science as omnipotent and omniscient; they volubly and publicly put their "faith" in science. Their "faith" affects other areas of modern life so that the word "scientific" has become a selling device for commercial advertisers and the "wonders of science" are revealed to children from the moment they begin school. Thus the myth of scientific omnipotence and omniscience is created and enlarged.

Perhaps the deification of science is unavoidable in our time. For science is complex, powerful and difficult to comprehend without long hours of study. Few people truly understand it. Those who are ignorant of science are mystified by it—and what mystifies us we tend to worship. Even trained scientists contribute to this deification process. They, having chosen a profession in science, quite humanly uphold its worth. Lawyers similarly uphold the legal profession, and doctors the medical profession. Humanists, devoted to the arts, frequently express their hatred of science and the inferred arrogance of its practitioners. Any group in conversation can develop heated arguments quickly when the subject of science versus the arts is introduced. In the ensuing uproar, tempers are lost, irrational statements are made and, within minutes, both the humanists and the scientists are acting like healthy human beings indistinguishable in their impassioned volubility. Which is a good thing.

Science is, after all, but the product of men's minds. It is accumulated knowledge of the material universe in which we live. If anything in science should be regarded with awe it is the revealed universe itself—not its discovery by men.

This is not to say that the story of our discoveries is unimportant. It is both important and exciting—and we can take limited pride and satisfaction in our accomplishments. We can also marvel at the ingenuity, persistence and imagination of the men who made significant discoveries from which we benefit.

Some of the men were what we call geniuses, while others were not. All of them, however, possessed a trait in common: an overwhelming absorption in their work. Whatever they were doing, wherever they were, some part of the investigator's mind was examining the problem confronting him.

All those who worked to answer a particular question labored under very human conditions which frequently included poverty, opposition, doubt and discouragement. In some cases the discoverer of a scientific principle either was unaware of what he had discovered or would not believe the evidence of his experiment because it contradicted established beliefs of his time. Other scientists found that after discovering something, they were unable to convince their colleagues of its truth; and still others shrank before the storm of controversy created by their radical theories.

The conflict of opposing theories is a common occurrence in science. To settle them today scientists put each of them to the ultimate test: experiment. If experiment verifies a theory it is regarded as "true" until a further theory is proposed which both includes and extends the older one. Thus the very heart of science today is experiment. Indeed, Isaac Newton stated that experiment was the beginning and end of science. Not until he presented the results of one of his first experiments with light did scientists begin to understand the true method of scientific investigation. When at last they grasped and used it, the door to knowledge of natural laws swung open and the age of scientific discovery began. Since that time, nearly three hundred years ago, men have learned more about the universe than in the entire history of man.

Living today amid all these discoveries and their applications, we frequently forget the circumstances surrounding the scientific investigations of the last three centuries. Then, knowledge in all areas of science was very limited. There were many theories but little data to be consulted and no guidepost to point the way to the answer to questions about electricity, chemistry, biology, aerodynamics, botany or any other area of interest to the investigator. Early modern scientists suffered under another large handicap. Communication among them was poor. If a man in Italy discovered an important fact it might be months or years before detailed knowledge of it reached England or the United States. And that very knowledge might have helped solve a problem confronting a scientist who was isolated in a distant land.

The difference today is striking. Scientific journals cover many fields of inquiry and report discoveries made in all countries. Prior to attacking a problem, a scientist today will have read all he can about work along similar lines of inquiry. In fact, he may read to his dismay that the project he is about to undertake has been completed by a scientist months before in another country.

Between the seventeenth and twentieth centuries, progress in solving problems and communicating the results accelerated. Interchange of ideas and discoveries of a scientific nature gave hope that a true international science might develop. But as the military aspects of nuclear fission became dominant, and men realized that political ends could be served by using new scientific knowledge, governments interrupted the channels of communications. Much work, government supported, became classified and unavailable for general dissemination. For beneath the ideal of free communication lies the instinct for self-preservation which must be acknowledged.

The experiments that have shaped our material lives today and that have posed innumerable social problems are numbered in the thousands. No single volume could describe them and any selection must omit important and perhaps equally influential experiments and discoveries. The experiments dramatized here were chosen because in some instances the immediate effects have been overwhelming and others, paradoxically, because their effects have not often been understood by the average person when the discovery was made. It is difficult for the nonscientist to foresee the consequences of some remote discovery on the frontier of science. This frontier lies in pure or basic research and it is the province of the scientists who understand that field of work. Until recently many laymen considered basic research (i.e., with no foreseeable goal in view) to be a waste of time. Yet it is from just such research that much of our modern world has come.

The Wright brothers' goal of building a flying machine is understandable, and the consequences of their success were almost predictable. But the consequences of Ernest Rutherford's experiments with the atom were not predictable at all—certainly not by the nonscientist. Yet both kinds of experiments are included here, for both have played and will continue to play important roles in the emerging drama of the human experience.

Isaac Newton: The Method of Science

Isaac Newton possessed what many people believe was the most outstanding intellect in human history. Over a span of forty years, this genius of science answered more fundamental questions about the physical universe than any man before or since his time. He invented mathematical systems which extended the usefulness of that science immeasurably. Eventually he organized, wrote and published the major results of his work in a three-volume work entitled *The Mathematical Principles of Natural Philosophy*. This book, today referred to simply as *The Principia,* is one of the great classics of all time.

His interest in physical science lay essentially in the study of gravitational force, motions of all kinds, the study of light— or opticks, as it was then known—and in chemistry.

By indirect, mathematical methods he formulated his Law of Universal Gravitation, which extended the idea of gravitational force from the regions near the earth to the most remote star in our galaxy. To the delight of astronomers of his day it explained why the planets moved in ellipses around the sun. Through painstaking experiment and mathematical reasoning, Newton precisely described the many motions of objects such as wheels, pendulums and flowing water. The results of this work laid the foundation for the science of mechanics. Mechanics is the subdivision of physics which deals with force and motion and it is the first part of physics ordinarily studied in schools and colleges.

Newton's interest in light produced the true explanation of the origin of colors and formulation of the laws which govern the behavior of light. By himself he established the science of spectroscopy or light analysis.

In chemistry Newton was not so fortunate. That science was still tangled with the ideas of magic and alchemy. Though Newton spent many years experimenting with flasks and distillation apparatus in his laboratory, he made no important discoveries in this field.

Newton's other large interest was mathematics. He invented the binomial theorem and the infinite series. Of wider usefulness was his invention of calculus, which he termed "The Method of Fluxions." The German mathematician, Gottfried Wilhelm von Leibniz, developed the same branch of mathematics independently of Newton and both men today are given credit. Calculus has proved to be one of the most useful and powerful mathematical tools ever invented.

As is always the case in science, one man's contribution inevitably owes a debt to those who worked a generation and more before in the same field. Newton, of course, built on the work of others who had preceded him and he freely acknowledged his indebtedness, remarking that if he had "seen" farther than others in his investigations, "it is by standing on the shoulders of giants." While this is true, it cannot detract from the momentous discoveries that he made.

A less tangible but equally important contribution made by Newton frequently is overlooked: his adherence to the true method of scientific investigation and his written admonition to others to stick to the true path leading to scientific knowledge. All of the precepts of the method of scientific investigation were not original with Newton but by following them and codifying them for others, he proved beyond question that the method he employed was the one leading to success.

School texts today emphasize the "scientific method" but rarely show what it entails. Manufacturers by the hundreds, in their hope to outsell their competitors, advertise their products as "scientifically tested." Scholars in fields other than science have been led to believe that the scientific method will produce conclusive results for them. This publicity given to science and its methods is the antithesis of true science.

In addition to following the scientific method of investigation himself, Newton spoke persuasively in support of it against the opinions of many of his contemporary scientists. In Book III of *The Principia*, titled "Rules of Reasoning in Philosophy," he set forth the fundamental methods of investigation. (The word "philosophy," or term "natural philosophy," can today be replaced by the word "science.")

Rule I

We are to admit no more causes of natural things than such as are both true and sufficient to explain their appearances.

To this purpose the philosophers (scientists) say that Nature does nothing in vain, and more is in vain when less will serve; for Nature is pleased with simplicity, and affects not the pomp of superfluous causes.

Rule II

Therefore to the same natural effects we must, as far as possible, assign the same causes.

As to respiration in a man and in a beast; the descent of stones in Europe and in America; the light of our culinary fire and of the sun; the reflection of light in the earth, and in the planets.

Rule III

The qualities of bodies, which admit neither intensification nor remission of degrees, and which are found to belong to all bodies within the reach of our experiments, are to be esteemed the universal qualities of all bodies whatsoever.

For since the qualities of bodies are only known to us by experiments, we are to hold for universal all such as universally agree with experiments; and such as are not liable to diminution can never be quite taken away. We are certainly not to relinquish the evidence of experiments for the sake of dreams and vain fictions of our own devising; nor are we to recede from the analogy of Nature, which is wont to be simple and always consonant to itself. . . .

It was Newton's strength that he saw clearly that these rules and all they imply must be obeyed; it is the average person's weakness that his own "dreams and vain fictions" will lead him to hope something is true and this hope will compel him to form a theory or hypothesis *before* he has completed any test or experiment of the idea.

Newton struggled to implant his rules in science. To a large degree he succeeded, but the very human tendency to imagine a scheme into which everything fitted persisted. Many first-rate scientists of his time held to the belief that the human mind was capable of understanding the universe without a detailed examination of it. The same tendency exists today.

Isaac Newton was born on Christmas Day in the year 1642 in Woolsthorpe, England. His father had died a few months before his birth and the young widow was faced with running the small farm alone and raising her son. Newton was born not only fatherless but also prematurely and underdeveloped.

This lack of physical development precluded his joining in the rough games of neighboring children and he spent the years of his early childhood playing alone, devising games that could be enjoyed in solitude. These physical circumstances set a pattern which persisted all his life. He enjoyed solitude and learned from his childhood experience to keep his own counsel.

Newton first attended nearby schools but since these were deficient he went at the age of twelve to Grantham, where he attended a more advanced school and boarded at the home of the local apothecary, Mr. Clark.

Newton's performance in schoolwork was not at all outstanding. His interest lay in his hobbies, which consisted of building ingenious mechanisms and conducting experiments of his own creation. He took great pleasure in designing a variety of kites and trying to get them to fly. He particularly delighted in devising lanterns that could be attached to the tails of kites and carried aloft with them. These he would fly at night, and many reports came from superstitious farmers nearby of seeing a comet in the heavens. Since comets in those days were believed to be omens from supernatural sources, Newton created considerable agitation among the people of Grantham.

He also built sundials and erected them in the Clarks' back yard. In his room he built a water clock which measured the hours by the flow of water from a small hole in the base of a water supply can. This type of clock, in use since ancient Egyptian days, did not rouse Newton's admiration. He commented in one of his childhood notebooks, where he kept scrupulous account of all his doings, that a small bit of foreign matter clogging the hole could throw the time piece off, and the chance of this happening was too great to make the clock a reliable instrument. In his room he also built a windmill and mounted it outside his window, and he schemed to build a treadmill so that captured mice might turn the windmill on calm days.

Newton's studies improved following an often reported incident of a boyhood fight with an older, larger schoolmate. Outraged by the boy's bullying of younger students, Newton forgot his own nonviolent nature long enough to whip the fellow. Not content with beating the boy physically, he studied hard enough to beat the boy academically. But once he had done this he stopped studying and soon his standing lowered. Whenever his failure was drawn to his attention, he would resume studying for a few days and regain the top position in class.

The urge to build and to experiment was part of Newton's nature and one of his earliest known experiments shows the originality of the mind in the young boy. Perhaps in testing his windmill he asked himself how he might measure the wind velocity. His idea for an experiment was as odd as it was original. On a windless day he drew a line on the ground and then jumped from it as far as he could. When the wind came up he would jump forward into it and then take another jump in the direction the wind was going. Knowing how far he could jump with no wind at all, he quickly calculated how much force the wind supplied when he jumped against it or with it. Since the force of the wind was a measure of its speed, he satisfied himself about wind velocities. Still, it must have bewildered his friends in later years to hear Newton refer to wind velocity as "so many feet of wind" as he invariably did.

The background of the Newton family was completely undistinguished. His father owned the small Woolsthorpe farm but it had never produced more than a bare living. His mother was of a good village family but nowhere in the family of either parent is there a clue to the originality and genius of Isaac

Newton. He was as singular a human being as William Shakespeare.

When Newton was three, his mother remarried, as much from economic necessity as anything else. She chose an older man, a lifelong bachelor, and she bore him several children. She moved from Woolsthorpe but did not give up the property. While Newton was in Grantham his stepfather died and the twice-widowed mother of Newton returned to Woolsthorpe with her children. Fortunately, her second husband had refurbished the Woolsthorpe farm at his wife's insistence, so she was not left entirely destitute. But her oldest son Isaac was now reaching an age when he might be expected to take on some responsibility. Newton left Grantham in 1656 and returned home to manage the farm. He had shown no aptitude for scholarship—except for his rare spurts of study—and his livelihood, it seemed, would come from farming. Nothing could have been more ill-advised. At home in Woolsthorpe, he would try to attend to business but his mind and attention seemed always to be elsewhere. On taking cattle to market he would never get a fair price. Even the undemanding chore of watching the cattle in the fields was beyond him. He would sit idly under a tree, lost in thought, while the cattle wandered away. In despair his mother sent him back to school to prepare for Cambridge University. He entered the university in 1661.

Newton's formal preparation had been adequate but not outstanding. His own efforts had not been outstanding either. Certainly nothing in his life or education had turned the country boy into a sophisticate. At Cambridge he found himself among many wealthy, well-born young men whose principal aim in life was to have a good time. Naturally he did not fit in. The silent, solitary young Newton became even more dedicated to solitude and to uncommunicativeness. When his roommate invited friends in for a party, Newton fled and took one more of his lonely walks. He was homesick for Woolsthorpe and he remained homesick all his undergraduate years at the University. At every opportunity he went home. Newton always had a deep love for his mother and only in her would he confide his dreams and ambitions. He could not tell her everything he thought, for she would not have understood. The subjects he studied were beyond her, although they were the usual ones for a university undergraduate of his day: Greek, Latin, history, science, plus, of course, mathematics.

During his first years at Cambridge, Newton was no more of a scholar than he had been at Grantham, at least so far as his professors could determine. Upon his arrival in 1661 he was assigned a tutor as is customary in English university study. Newton's tutor was the well-known scholar, scientist and theologian Isaac Barrow. He held the important Lucasian Chair of mathematics, an endowed post. Able, sympathetic and intelligent, Isaac Barrow watched his young protégé Newton as he made his first contact with the world outside of Woolsthorpe. It was a world of war, of change, of great discovery and innovation, of stubbornly held traditions.

The man who had shaped the science of Newton's time lived nearly two thousand years before the seventeenth century. For it was the Greek philosopher Aristotle whose work and theories held sway for the two milleniums of human history that intervened. In the fields of logic, of botany, of government Aristotle made important contributions. But in the area of physics he made many mistakes and formed false theories which persisted. The writings of Aristotle passed first from Greece to Arabia. They were discovered there by western men hundreds of years later and the new knowledge that they gave

Europe, which was then emerging from the Dark Ages, was so startling that learned men everywhere accepted Aristotle's teachings as true and inviolable. At the time of their discovery by Europe, the Catholic Church was the only authority in religious matters and was the source of all education. The schools and universities scattered from Italy to England were owned and operated by the Roman Church.

Through the Dark Ages the protectors of knowledge were the monks and priests who kept alive the ideas, the books, the entire heritage of the past. And Aristotle's writings were a great part of the past. It was natural that the Church would accept his theories in all fields as being true. Just as, naturally, the churchmen would reject theories that countered Aristotle. In short, the errors in physics that Aristotle committed had become part of the accepted teaching of the Church.

The source of Aristotle's errors in physics lay in his dislike for experiment. He loved to theorize, to produce a plausible scheme of how things really were in nature and then create arguments to show how everything fitted into it. So persuasive were his words that few scholars thought to question their truth. But in the sixteenth century men like Galileo, Kepler, Copernicus and some others had begun to question Aristotle. The Church reacted vigorously, and for many years the old beliefs and the new ideas clashed head on.

The old beliefs still were taught in the universities of Europe. And though many areas of Germany, France and all of England had formally broken with the Roman Church, they took the educational scheme of the Roman Church with them and continued to teach the ancient science of Aristotle. Even when Newton was at Cambridge, the idea that the earth lay at the center of the solar system and everything revolved around it was still being taught.

A few men, notably Galileo, stood for experiment and mathematical analysis of the results as the true way of science. But
the love of imagining an explanation for the physical world
persisted. This is not to say that man's imagination is useless
in science. Properly used, it has advanced knowledge tre-
mendously by putting together *observed* occurrences in
original patterns which then can stand the test of experiment.
Its improper use is summed up in the word "daydreaming."

Newton lived at a time when the new approach to science
was making great headway against the currents of the past.
Interest in exploration had opened new lands and brought
wealth to Europe. The wealth whetted the appetites of governments for more. The great voyages had created interest in
navigational problems and this inevitably led to the use of
mathematics to solve them.

Classic education before Newton's time had placed mathematics low on the list of civilized accomplishments. It held the
place in men's esteem that skill in solving puzzles does now:
amusing, but not useful. But when Galileo pointed out that
mathematics was the only certain way to state the truth of a
physical principle, and men began to use mathematics to solve
physical problems and to state as yet unsolvable problems,
science began to grow at a more rapid pace.

Other circumstances contributed to the rapid growth of
science. Not the least of these was the means of communicating
among scientists. Printing and wide distribution of new ideas
and information helped science to grow as it did all other fields
of learning. And scientists were forming their own organizations outside the universities, which lagged behind the spectacular advance of new knowledge. The Royal Scientific Society
was formed in England in 1662, the year after Newton entered

Cambridge. Papers were presented at regular meetings and when some novel idea or experiment came to the attention of the members, the Society recorded and printed the event. Copies were sent to other societies in France, Germany and Italy, as well as to such outstanding individuals as Descartes, the great French mathematician, to Christian Huygens, the Dutch scientist, and Wilhelm von Leibniz, German mathematician and philosopher.

At Cambridge, Newton became interested in the study of light and began to read the outstanding text of the day, *Opticks,* by Johann Kepler. In the course of studying Kepler's mathematics Newton found difficulty in following the geometric proofs. Accordingly, he undertook to learn geometry, a subject he had formerly disliked, and this led him to Descartes and the advances that man had made in the subject. So intense became Newton's admiration for the rigor and thoroughness of geometric proof that he used it in much of his later writing and explanation of his findings.

Newton's tutor, Isaac Barrow, was himself interested in the study of light and Newton read several papers prepared by the older man. Not content with examining merely the theory of light, Newton "put it to the test." He designed and built telescopes, grinding his own lenses slowly and painstakingly by hand. In examining light at first hand, Newton discovered that however perfectly he ground his lenses, the images formed by them were not perfectly distinct. A fringe of color appeared on the image screen and he could do nothing to eliminate it or focus the images as distinctly as he wanted.

In 1665, near the end of Newton's undergraduate years at Cambridge, bubonic plague struck London, killing over thirty thousand people. The plague spread to the rural areas of England and the Cambridge officials decided the university would have to be closed to protect the students. They were all sent home.

For nearly eighteen months the plague alternately increased and abated and during most of that time Newton was home at his beloved Woolsthorpe with his mother, his younger step-sisters and brothers. Outwardly he had not changed since leaving four years before. He still seemed unable to cope with the daily affairs of the farm. He dreamed beneath the apple trees in the orchard or wandered in solitude across the meadows. But those months of Newton's life were the most productive ones he ever spent. For it was during this time of enforced isolation that Newton succeeded in solving several problems that had been in his mind for years. At the age of twenty-four, Newton saw the way toward success in answering the question: Why do the planets move in their particular paths? And although he was not to perfect and publish the Law of Universal Gravitation for many years, he satisfied himself by mathematical calculation that he had found the answer "pretty nearly." He developed his new mathematics, the calculus as well as the binomial theorem and infinite series. He also carried on his experiments with light. He had brought home his tele-scopes and lens-grinding apparatus. And he was thoroughly convinced that the failure of his lenses to focus clearly was not the fault of the glass. He believed the true cause lay in the nature of light itself. He set about experimenting to prove his suspicion.

The accomplishments of Newton during these months are almost incredible. Had he done only one of the things he did, he would have earned a place in the history of science. But to have done all of them then, or at least to have seen the path to eventual perfection of proof of his ideas, is the astounding thing. What is even more incomprehensible is the fact that he made no announcement to anyone about his discoveries.

In later years when pressed to recall the events of those months, Newton wrote laconically, "In the beginning of the year 1665 I found the method for approximating series and the rule for reducing any [power] of any binomial to such a series. The same year in May I found the method of tangents of Gregory and Slusius and in November the direct method of Fluxions [calculus] and the next year in January had the Theory of Colors, and in May following I had entrance into the inverse method of Fluxions and in the same year I began to think of gravity extending to the orb of the Moon . . . and having thereby compared the force requisite to keep the Moon in her orb [orbit] with the force of gravity at the surface of the earth, and found them to answer pretty nearly. . . . All this was in the two plague years of 1665 and 1666, for in those days I was in the prime of my age for invention, and minded Mathematicks and philosophy (science) more than at any time since."

Newton returned to Cambridge for a brief period in 1666 when the plague was not so virulent, went back to Woolsthorpe and then returned once more to Cambridge in 1667. He was no longer an undergraduate. By this time he had written several papers on some of his mathematical discoveries and Isaac Barrow, in 1668, resigned his post as Lucasian professor of mathematics in favor of Newton—who was then only twenty-six.

He continued his experiments with light, although by this time he knew the answer to something that had puzzled scientists for many years. The question was: What is the source of color? Investigation had shown that a triangular glass prism would admit sunlight at one face of the prism and emit the rainbow colors of the spectrum from the face from which the light emerged. What was there in the glass material that produced the colors?

As Newton had learned from his lens-grinding experience, the prism merely acted to separate the colors which were in the sunlight. This characteristic of glass caused the blurring of images and produced the color fringes around images formed by glass lenses. Knowing this, Newton turned to another kind of telescope: the reflecting telescope. He used a highly polished concave metal surface and by employing the laws of light reflection brought an image to focus that had no color fringe and was not distorted in any way since the light did not enter or emerge from a glass prism.

When he had built a workable reflecting telescope he wrote a paper on it for the Royal Society and sent it to London. The response he got was flattering and, for one so accustomed to solitude and lack of acceptance, overwhelming. It was Newton's first taste of praise and recognition by older, more distinguished scientists. He then decided to reveal his theory of the origin of colors. In a letter to the Society secretary, Newton said that he was preparing a paper on "the oddest, if not the most considerable detection, which hath hitherto been made in the operations of nature. . . ."

He then began to organize the results of his lengthy experiment with prisms—the experiment that established the science of spectroscopy or light analysis.

From prehistoric times men had watched the heavens and noticed the movement of planets, the moon and sun. The patterns of stars were observed and recorded. The ancient Chaldeans made extensive observations of motions of heavenly bodies and kept voluminous records. Not unnaturally, primitive scientists attributed supernatural causes to these motions and interpreted them as signs to men on earth. The belief that planetary motions and juxtapositions influenced men's destinies produced the "religion" of astrology which persisted down through Newton's time.

Light from these stars and planets was believed to travel at infinite speed. For no matter how distant a light source might be from an observer on earth, there seemed to be no time lapse between sending and receiving a light signal.

Ptolemy, the Egyptian scientist and mathematician, studied the behavior of light rays, and though many scientists followed him in that study, no adequate explanation could be given for the "thing" called light.

Newton and many of his contemporaries thought that light was a stream of small particles sent out by a source. These particles appeared to travel in straight lines. When they struck the eye of an observer they produced the sensation called sight.

Opponents of this theory included Christian Huygens who held that light was a wave motion similar to water waves. But since water waves need the medium of water to exist and travel through, there had to be a medium for light waves to travel through. Men named this undiscovered medium "the aether." The concept of an ether and a search for it in the space between objects was vigorously pursued by the best scientists of Newton's day. He himself was inclined to believe in its existence. And it was not until the end of the nineteenth century that the search for an ether was dropped.

An interest in and study of light naturally included a study of color. The ability of a prism to produce a rainbow-like spectrum of color had long been known. Many scientists who believed that the glass was the source of the color performed experiments with prisms and lenses, discovering some of the properties of light, but not the source of colors.

Unknown to anyone, Newton began his investigations into light and his efforts covered a period of several years. When he was through, he had examined the properties of light more thoroughly than anyone before him. And whether light was a wave or a stream of particles was not the question. He had rigorously studied the phenomena of light itself and tested everything he could by experiment.

Working with prisms and using sunlight admitted through a small opening in the shutter of his room, Newton examined every phenomenon of light that came to his attention. One of the things he observed and wondered about was this: If light came from a spherical source like the sun and passed through a prism it should produce a circular image. But sunlight passing through the prism produced what at first glance seemed to be an oblong image. Why? Though many other men had examined the spectra produced by prisms, none had pondered for any length of time over this particular question. On examining the oblong image carefully, Newton saw that it was not truly rectangular. Actually, it had the shape of a race track— long parallel sides and semicircular ends.

Eventually, Newton determined the cause of this phenomenon. Each color composing white light was refracted or "bent" through the prism at a slightly different angle—and each produced a circular image. But the circular images overlapped and the resulting image was a spectrum of overlapping circles, so many of them that they produced the parallel sides of the image. The circles on each end of the spectrum were not overlapped by further colored circles and hence defined the semicircular ends. It was like placing a number of pennies in a row and having each penny overlap the next.

Painstakingly Newton produced and measured spectra. He let the colored lights fall on black, white and variously colored surfaces. He used prisms in combinations and allowed the light to strike the prism faces at various angles. He measured everything. He turned the prisms until the light striking the prism face was totally reflected and he measured all angles of reflection and refraction as he proceeded. He passed sunlight through small slits made in black paper and sometimes allowed light to fall on a prism through two slits simultaneously.

In one of his crucial experiments, the one that showed most convincingly that all colors were contained in white light, he passed sunlight through one prism, separating it as always into the various colors of the spectrum, then he placed a second prism beyond the first so that the separated colors entered the second prism and emerged as white light again.

When he was through Newton wrote a report on his findings. He presented all the material much as classic geometry is presented in textbooks today. He laid down definitions of terms. He stated as axioms certain known properties of light such as the fact that the angles of incidence and reflection were equal for light striking a reflecting surface. He then set forth his various propositions, the first of which read: Lights which differ in color differ also in degrees of refrangibility (refraction or bending through a prism). Following each proposition he placed the all-important words: The Proof by Experiments.

The paper that Newton prepared for the Royal Society was a model report of his investigations. Read today, in the light of many later scientific papers, it can scarcely be improved on. It displayed results of his work clearly and completely.

Galileo had published the results of his experimental work in a chatty dialogue style patterned after Plato's persuasive method of presenting ideas and arguments; Newton merely gave a step-by-step explanation of what he had done. It was a completely objective presentation of material. It was so different from the ornate prose styles of the day that it chilled his readers. Many of them were repelled by its "cold-bloodedness."

But here was the true scientific method, stated explicitly and completely for the first time. Observe, experiment, and deduce conclusions mathematically or with testable logic. Report the results and the conclusions without personal embellishment or bias.

To Newton this method was so natural he cannot be said to have "invented it." It was the true method, and when he had completed his paper for the Royal Society, Newton sent it in confidently. For he knew that the only way to disprove his conclusions was to show by experiment that he was wrong. And he had completed successfully all the significant experiments.

The reception of his paper by the Royal Society was quite different from what Newton had hoped. It created controversy. Some members agreed with its conclusions; some disagreed. None realized that arguments against Newton's results were futile. Those who suspected the futility of such argument were vaguely affronted. Who was this young upstart to deny them the interest and amusement of argument for or against the paper?

Newton was appalled by the controversy. When critics wrote angrily disagreeing with his conclusions, Newton patiently wrote long letters trying to explain his work more clearly. Actually this was not necessary—and Newton understood it. No one could upset his conclusions save by experiment. He was at once repelled by and involved with the attacks. So strong was his desire to be accepted that he hoped to persuade opponents of his work that he was right. In nearly all these attempts he failed.

One result of this criticism of his work was to convince Newton that making public the results of his work was not worth the effort. Due to this conviction historians have had a difficult time piecing together the precise steps Newton took in solving other important problems, for his childhood trait of uncommunicativeness was reinforced in the man he had become. He had no desire to become involved with his scientific contemporaries and, in a sense, he turned his back on them and on most of their efforts to draw him into controversy or discussion. He remained at Cambridge, isolated from his time —but still actively working on science.

The ideas about gravity which he had had in the plague years of 1665–66 finally came to maturity and Newton, urged on by a young friend, Edmund Halley, began to prepare a paper for the Society in 1684. In it he organized all his studies on motion. As he worked, however, the "paper" grew, became more detailed and eventually emerged as his great work, *The Mathematical Principles of Natural Philosophy*. *The Principia* consisted of three volumes and was written in Latin, which was the language of scholars of that day. The book was published in 1687 and it established Newton as one of the immortals of science. From that time forward the habit of idly hypothesizing about natural occurrences began to die out. Experiment and mathematical analysis became the accepted way of science. Newton stated the method clearly when he wrote, ". . . the best and safest method of philosophizing seems to be, first to enquire diligently into the properties of things, and of establishing those properties by experiments, and then to proceed more slowly to hypothesis for the explanation of them."

Although Newton turned from a direct study of science and mathematics, he remained a giant in both areas to the end of his days. In 1696 Johann Bernoulli, a Swiss physicist, offered a prize to anyone who could solve within six months a mathematical problem he proposed. Newton solved it overnight. And in 1716 his co-discoverer of calculus, Leibniz, proposed a problem to English mathematicians to see how skilled they were. Newton solved the problem with only a few hours' effort.

The total effect of Newton on his own time and on all succeeding generations is impossible to state precisely. But from the principles he uncovered and through the method that he championed, western man learned more of the world he lives in than had been dreamed of before. Newtonian principles of motion allow us to design and build the machinery that is the hallmark of the industrial age. His analysis of light opened many new fields to study. The science of spectroscopy or light analysis has given us a way to examine those ultimate particles of matter, the atoms, and the knowledge that came from that examination produced the atomic age and modern physics.

On March 27, 1727, Sir Isaac Newton died at the age of eighty-five. His body is buried in Westminster Abbey. It had housed one of the most extraordinary minds in human history. In Wordsworth's words,

". . . a mind forever
    Voyaging through strange seas of thought, alone."

Michael Faraday: Electricity and Magnetism

Of all the phenomena of nature, two of the most difficult to understand are electricity and magnetism. Even now, with all our use of these two properties of matter, all our instruments to measure them and our knowledge of their characteristics, they remain ultimately unexplained. At the beginning of the nineteenth century very little was known of electricity and magnetism and what was known—or guessed at—was in no sense of the word useful.

One of the most original and thorough experimenters of all times, Michael Faraday, spent his life investigating these phenomena. In the course of his investigations he discovered many of the interactions of electricity and magnetism through experiment. From a practical standpoint, he opened the way to the development of electric motors and generators without which modern life would be quite different. In terms of pure scientific research and interest in science per se, he was the first to propose what we call today the "field theory" of matter. His proposal and the later development of it led to Einstein's theory of relativity, the full consequences of which have not yet been felt. The results of Faraday's lifetime of work were published in a huge seven-volume set of books appropriately titled *Experimental Researches in Electricity*.

The importance of Faraday's idea of fields can hardly be overestimated. We are accustomed today to speak of the gravitational field of the earth or of some other celestial body like the sun. We know that to send a satellite into orbit, we must consider this gravitational field of the earth. To send a rocket to the moon or to Mars, scientists must calculate the effect of not only the earth's field but also the fields of the sun, the planet toward which they send the rocket and the fields of other members of our solar system.

Magnets influence certain objects in the regions surrounding them and scientists speak of the magnetic field about the magnet itself. Electrical fields are equally evident. An object charged with static electricity will influence uncharged nearby objects that lie within the electrical field. These regions of influence about matter were first conceived and demonstrated by Michael Faraday. In fact it was his firm belief that gravitational, magnetic, electrical and light phenomena were fundamentally similiar and sprang from the same cause. And although we do not know this for a fact today, there is much evidence to support Faraday's belief.

Scientists of Newton's time were divided over the argument that an ether existed, filling space between matter, between all objects whether they were planets and stars or merely two rocks resting on the earth. Believers in the existence of an ether held that in order for gravitational force to be exerted by the sun on the earth and other planets, there had to be some contact between them, something had to reach out and touch the earth from the sun so that the force could travel the 93,000,000 miles between them. Light, it was also argued, needed an ether to travel the great distances it did. Those who disbelieved in an ether held that forces "acting at a distance" did not need anything to be active on an object. Such forces as had been observed were gravitational, electrical and magnetic in nature.

Faraday's field idea offered another and more testable explanation. He elaborated on the idea all his life and, in essence, stated that material objects were not bounded by their visible edges. He believed that matter itself extended beyond the visible or touchable edges of objects, that it permeated space and filled it. From his point of view, there was no such thing as empty space or "the void," as it has been called poetically.

His concept was so radical at the time he proposed it that it, like other revolutionary ideas, did not find immediate acceptance. Scientists and philosophers—like all human beings—resist any change in the concepts they have held all their lives. In Faraday's time Newtonian physics had so filled the minds of scientists that another and apparently different idea could scarcely find great numbers of believers.

Yet Faraday's idea persisted. Gradually the truth of what it was trying to say became evident and irrefutable. The means by which this was accomplished was that by which Newton established his theories: experiment.

The early part of the nineteenth century during which Faraday lived frequently has been called the beginning of the scientific age in which we now live. There is never a definite calendar date when such periods begin or end in history, but the latter part of the eighteenth century and the first half of the nineteenth contain many important dates of scientific discovery.

Man had begun to look on the world as a huge and complex machine which was only material—and had begun to regard himself as somewhat less important a figure in the universe than before. Copernicus, the great Polish astronomer, had shown that the earth was not at the center of the universe with everything revolving around it. He and other astronomers had proved that the earth was rather small and relatively inconsequential in the myriad stars of the galaxy. Newton's work showed that the solar system was moving with the regularity of a clock, according to mathematical formulas that he had worked out. The mysteries of chemical action were shown to be nothing but interactions of matter, proceeding by definite and provable rules. Everything of importance about the universe was believed to have been discovered and the term "scientific outlook" came to mean one which viewed everything as mere matter—including man himself. In the great discoveries of that time, man had been "cut down to size" and he began to doubt the credos that had sustained and inspired him in the past. His ego had been severely damaged by the knowledge that he was not at the center of the world.

In the practical world of commerce and everyday life, science was beginning to bring benefits. The industrial age had begun and machines began to do the work men had to do formerly. The principles of operation of those machines had come from scientific inquiries and scientific answers to questions of chemistry, heat, light, mechanics and electricity.

Michael Faraday was born in 1791 in London of a poor family. His father was a blacksmith. In that day and time, to be born into such a family was to have no hope, or even thought, of rising to any higher level of existence. Most boys who were born then under similar circumstances went to work early and learned the trades their fathers could teach them. And as a youngster, Faraday did not think beyond that.

He attended school only long enough to learn to read, write and do simple arithmetic. He never received more formal education. His first job was that of an errand boy to a bookseller and from this job he was "promoted" to an apprentice book-binder in the shop—without pay. The benefit he would reap from this work was suspected by neither Faraday nor the bookseller. During his days in the shop, Faraday was exposed to a wide variety of books and he began reading works of science that came to his attention. He learned some chemistry from one book and read all there was on electricity in the *Encyclopaedia Britannica.*

By this time his obvious lack of learning was evident to Faraday and he set about the difficult task of isolated self-education. He practiced writing and speaking, using the books of the shop as his texts and guides. He sought and found help in learning to draw. His ambition continued and when he became the guest of one of the bookshop customers at a lecture at the Royal Society he was so determined not to miss what was said that he took quantities of notes throughout the discussion. The lecture that day was given by Sir Humphry Davy, one of England's leading scientists.

When he was back at work in the bookshop, Faraday completed the notes from the lecture and sketched diagrams of the demonstration equipment that Davy had used. Then he sent the "report" to Davy with a letter begging permission to be allowed to work for him. It was the sincere impulse of a young man who was fascinated with science and who was determined to get into the field despite all handicaps.

Davy rejected his application abruptly. He was an important man and could scarcely be bothered by ignorant apprentices or their dreams. But a few weeks after Faraday had applied and been turned down, a laboratory assistant at the Society was fired—and Davy thought of the eager young Faraday in the bookshop. He sent for Faraday and the young man found himself working beside a great scientist as his laboratory assistant.

One of his first tasks was to accompany Davy on a prolonged tour of Europe. It was the best kind of education an apprentice scientist of that day, or any other, could have had. Davy traveled through Germany, France, Holland, Belgium, Switzerland and Italy meeting and consulting with leading scientists of those countries. Faraday joyously soaked up all the information he could. Fortunately the science of that day required less mathematical explanation than it does now and Faraday, despite his deficiency in mathematics, could understand most of what was being discussed and could store the knowledge in his mind and notebooks for future use.

For seven years Faraday worked as Davy's laboratory assistant. His own interest lay in electricity, magnetism and chemistry. He read all the background material available on work in those fields, eventually writing a paper of his own titled *Historical Sketch of Electromagnetism*. By the time he was thirty, he had contributed papers to the *Quarterly Journal of Science* on chemistry and electricity and at that time he began writing the results of his major work in electromagnetism.

The germ of Faraday's idea for "fields" can be easily located in the work of William Gilbert. A Fellow of St. John's, Cambridge, and physician to the queen, William Gilbert stood nearly alone among the learned men of England during the first years of the seventeenth century. In 1600 he published a book on magnetism titled *De Magnete* in which he describes in detail experiments with magnets. Among them is the simple experiment of placing a magnet beneath a sheet of paper, sprinkling the paper with iron filings and then tapping the sheet. The filings, momentarily jostled, respond to the force of the magnet and form a pattern of curved lines about the magnet. These seem to be proceeding from one pole of the magnet, forming a closed path to the other pole. Thus a long straight iron bar that has been magnetized will show lines proceeding from one end outward into the region beyond the magnet and then bending rather sharply at first to run nearly parallel to the bar. When they approach the opposite end, they bend around and appear to enter the magnet again.

William Gilbert undertook his investigations in magnetism in response to a very practical need. He lived during the age of exploration, and questions of navigation, of compass navigating in particular, were of immense importance. In the true spirit of experimentation Gilbert, the learned professor at Cambridge, visited foundries and ironworks, asking questions of the workers and learning how to operate a forge himself. He talked to sailors and captains of vessels in the English ports and he got from his labors a true picture of the problems facing the mariners, and the nature of iron and compasses. As a result he was struck by the fact that the earth itself appears to act like a giant magnet and he put forth that idea in his book.

He also wrote of the regions around magnets which gave Faraday his idea for fields and for the means to describe them with "lines of force" which came from the lines formed by the iron filings.

The phenomenon of magnetism, of course, had been known for centuries and crude compasses had guided sailors of antiquity. But Gilbert's work summed up all that was known on the subject and, more importantly, contributed new knowledge that had been gained by Gilbert in the modern scientific manner: by experiment. His accomplishment so early in the history of modern science is truly astonishing.

Gilbert also worked with what we today call static electricity. This property of materials had also been known for many years. It had been found in Greek days that if amber were rubbed with a bit of cat's fur, the amber was capable of attracting small bits of straw. If an especially strong charge of electricity could be built up, a spark might be observed when the charged object was brought near an uncharged one.

Scientists in the eighteenth century developed an idea that electricity was a fluid which, somehow or other, could flow from one object to another. When one object was lacking some of this fluid it was charged; if another object had an excess of electrical fluid it too was charged but with an opposite charge. To distinguish between the two kinds of charge which could be produced, scientists gave the titles of positive and negative— terms we still have with us today in electrical considerations.

When it became possible to develop and store a charge of electricity of considerable size, larger and larger sparks were produced and they, of course, crackled as they proceeded through the atmosphere to an uncharged body. Scientists quickly related the sight and sound of electrical discharges to the lightning strokes and thunder accompanying many storms. Although much investigation into electrical "fluid" and its actions was known in the eighteenth century, there was little or no practical use to which the information could be put. When the Leyden jar was developed, the charge it produced caused a fashionable stir among the aristocracy of Europe. The Leyden jar is a glass container the inside and outside surfaces of which are coated with tin foil. When charged, the two layers of foil hold a sizable and dangerous amount of electrical "fluid." The ladies and lords of the courts of Europe apparently enjoyed the sensation of being numbed by an electric shock, and demonstrations were in favor for some time. One of the most spectacular shows put on was that of a row of soldiers standing rigidly with clasped hands as the Leyden jar was discharged. The entire rank of soldiers would experience the shock almost simultaneously and would leap into the air as their muscles reacted.

Curiosity about electrical discharges engaged the attention of many scientists, among them Benjamin Franklin, who drew lightning from the sky. And while there was intense interest in electricity, there seemed to be no wide application for its action.

Both magnetism and electricity were known to exert forces on objects at some distance from the magnet or charged object. But the relationship between electricity and magnetism was not known until Hans Christian Oersted discovered it. According to legend he was trying to disprove any relationship between magnetism and electricity when instead he opened the door to many discoveries which form the subject of electromagnetism today. He found that when an electric current flowed in a wire, a magnetic field *always* could be detected near the wire. By 1820 the production of an electric current in a conductor could be realized with a simple chemical battery. The electric "fluid" flowed through a wire and Oersted placed a small compass above or below such a wire and connected the wire to a battery. The compass needle was deflected while the current flowed; it turned until it stood motionless at right angles to the current-carrying wire. The deduction was obvious: when a current flows in a conductor, a magnetic field is created about the conductor. Tests with the compass showed that the magnetic field was circular about a long straight wire and that its influence or force on a compass varied inversely as the square of the distance between conductor and compass. Thus if a force of one unit existed one inch from the wire, a force of one-fourth unit existed two inches from the wire.

The French scientist, André Ampère, investigated Oersted's discovery exhaustively and formed a great many useful and accurate equations. He also discovered that a current in a wire would affect not only a compass needle, it would also affect a nearby conductor which was carrying a current.

It remained for Michael Faraday to ask an apparently obvious question rising from Oersted's discovery. If a current flowing in a wire creates a magnetic field around the wire, would the creation of a magnetic field produce a current in a wire?

To find the answer to that question—and to many others about electricity and magnetism—Faraday began an exhaustive series of experiments. The year was 1824. The results of his first attempt he duly recorded in detail in the following words:

"About 26 feet of copper wire one-twentieth of an inch in diameter were wound round a cylinder of wood as a helix, the different spires (loops) of which were prevented from touching by a thin interposed twine. This helix was covered with calico, and then a second wire applied in the same manner. In this way twelve helices were superposed, each containing an average length of wire of 27 feet and all in the same direction. The first, third, fifth, seventh, ninth and eleventh of these helices were connected at their extremities end to end so as to form one helix; the others were connected in a similar manner; and thus two principal helices were produced, closely interposed, having the same direction, not touching anywhere, and each containing 155 feet in length of wire.

"One of these helices was connected to a galvanometer [a detecting device for electric currents] the other with a voltaic battery of ten pairs of plates four inches square, with double coppers and well charged; yet not the slightest sensible deflection of the galvanometer-needle could be observed."

So Faraday failed on his first attempt. He tried again, this time using copper wire on one set of helices and iron wire on the other. Still he failed to produce a current in one helix separated from the other which carried a current.

In these first attempts Faraday was trying to "induce" a current in one coil or helix of wire by sending a strong current through a second coil placed nearby.

Undeterred by his failure Faraday increased the length of wire in the helices and the voltage of his battery until, as he put it, "the active power of the battery was proved to be great, by its heating the whole of its own helix, and by the brilliancy of the discharge when made through charcoal." All he could notice from the new arrangement was that when he closed the switch on the coil connected to the battery, the needle of the galvanometer was moved slightly—but then it returned to its original position indicating only that slight pulse of current was generated and it quickly died away. He discovered, too, that when he opened the switch of his battery circuit, the needle was deflected briefly in the opposite direction.

To all appearances he had failed. Such a slight, brief current as he had been able to produce was of no possible use nor did it support his idea that the magnetic field around his current-carrying coil would induce a strong continuous flow of current in a conductor placed nearby.

We know today that Faraday was within a hairsbreadth of having the answer to his question within his grasp. But for six or seven years repeated attempts failed. The answer lay in his notes and in his mind. When he had closed the switch, there had been a brief pulse of current; when he opened it, there had been an equally feeble and brief pulse of current in the opposite direction.

During the years Faraday worked on many other projects, but between 1824 and 1831 he did discover a way to make the brief pulse of current much stronger. Originally he had wound his helices around wooden or glass cylinders or rings. On one occasion he used an iron ring, a material subject to magnetization, and he found that on closing and opening the switch on his first coil with the galvanometer connected to the second coil, the needle moved much farther than before. Its motion, however, was still very brief.

Continued investigation led him to place the iron ring or core, about which his separated helices were wrapped, between the poles of a magnet. He found that still he could not produce a permanent current in the second coil.

Historians date the first realization of the true situation and solution to his problem by Faraday August 29, 1831. From that day on, Faraday worked at a furious pace. The iron ring he had been using was magnetized by the current flowing in the wire wrapped around it. While this magnetization was being accomplished, a current flowed in the wire forming the second helix. But when the iron ring was completely magnetized, the current stopped flowing in the second helix.

At this point Faraday began to use his idea of the field about magnets and electric charges. Oersted had discovered that a current flowing in a wire created a magnetic field about the wire. Soft iron, when placed in a magnetic field of influence, becomes itself magnetized. The idea Faraday had was that as the process of magnetizing the iron ring was going on, the lines of force were being built up or created in the region about the ring. Since the second coil was in this region, these lines of force intercepted or cut across the wires of the second helix. During this time current flowed in the second coil.

The key to the puzzle was the *motion* of the lines, not their mere existence. In Oersted's experiment a *moving* current of electricity had created a magnetic field about the wire that persisted as long as the electricity *moved* through the wire. In order for the reverse effect to be obtained—that is, to establish a permanent current in a wire within a magnetic field—the field or lines of force had to be "in motion" relative to the wire.

This could be accomplished in two ways. Faraday had already found the first method. By magnetizing an iron ring he built up lines of force about it. In the process the lines cut across the second helix and produced a current. The second method he found about seven weeks after his realization that motion of the magnetic field was the cause of the induced current.

He wrapped 220 feet of copper wire around a hollow paper cylinder forming a single helix. The ends of this he connected to a galvanometer. Then he simply took a permanent bar magnet and pushed one pole of it into the cylinder. Since the magnetic field moved forward with the magnet, the lines of force cut the coil of wire and the galvanometer showed a deflection. When he withdrew the magnet a current was also detected but in the opposite direction. Faraday also found that the speed of plunging the magnet into the cylinder affected the amount of galvanometer deflection which measured the amount of current. In other words, Faraday discovered the essential principle of electromagnetic induction with a magnet: the speed of cutting lines of force. If, for example, 1000 of these imaginary lines were cut per second, a certain current would be induced in the coil. If 2000 were cut per second, twice as much current would be induced. He also found that it did not matter whether the magnet moved and the coil was stationary or vice versa. If he held the magnet stationary and pushed the hollow cylinder with the coil on it over the magnet, he got a current of electricity.

His next problem was a practical one: How could you keep a magnet or a conductor constantly in motion with respect to the other? The obvious solution is circular motion of either a magnet or a coil of wire. But a coil of wire cannot be constantly turned without becoming hopelessly entangled and eventually breaking. And if a magnet is turned inside a coil, the result will be a pulse of current in one direction and then a pulse in another.

Today we recognize this as alternating current but in Faraday's time only direct current obtained from chemical batteries was known. He, therefore, naturally wanted to produce such a uni-directional current.

His solution was ingenious but crude. He took a copper disk mounted on a brass axle and coated the edge of the disk and a portion of it near the axle with mercury. The liquid mercury adheres to the copper yet retains its liquidity so that a wire touching the coated area has a good electrical contact. That done, he mounted two bar magnets so that the north pole of one was half an inch from the south pole of the other. "All these arrangements being made," Faraday reported, "the copper disk was adjusted, the small magnetic poles being about half an inch apart and the edge of the plate inserted about half their width between them. One of the galvanometer wires was passed twice or thrice loosely around the brass axis of the plate, and the other attached to a conductor which itself was retained by the hand in contact with the amalgamated (mercury-coated) edge of the disk at the part immediately between the magnetic poles. Under these conditions all was quiescent, and the galvanometer exhibited no effect. But the instant the plate moved, the galvanometer was influenced, and by revolving the plate quickly the needle could be deflected 90° or more.

"It was difficult under the circumstances to make the contact between the conductor and the edge of the revolving disk uniformly good and extensive; it was also difficult in the first experiments to obtain a regular velocity of rotation; both these causes tended to retain the needle in a continual state of vibration; but no difficulty existed in ascertaining to which side it was deflected, or generally, about what line it vibrated. Afterwards when the experiments were made more carefully, a permanent deflection of the needle of nearly 45° could be sustained.

"Here therefore was demonstration of the production of a permanent current of electricity by ordinary magnets."

Faraday had invented the electric generator.

By mechanically turning the disk—a conductor—within a magnetic field, he caused a current to flow in the conductor. Eventual research discovered the converse of this procedure which resulted in the electric motor. That is, if a current flows in a conductor which is in a magnetic field, the wire will be acted on by a force tending to push it one way or another. If the conductor so placed is wrapped around an axle, the axle will turn—and mechanical work can be done by the turning axle.

To explain the occurrences he had created, Faraday developed and clarified his ideas of the fields of influence about magnets. He measured the strengths of the fields and assigned directions to the lines of force. He showed diagrammatically which direction a conductor would be pushed by interacting magnetic fields. He was not a mathematician and so had to be content with his visualization of "lines of force" or "fields." The important theoretical benefit of these concepts was not evident until the early part of the twentieth century when Einstein developed mathematical equations for the field theory which now dominates an important part of physics.

Another mathematician, however, came eventually to Faraday's assistance. James Clerk Maxwell, a university-trained mathematician, studied Faraday's drawings of fields and read all the results Faraday so painstakingly wrote up in detail. Maxwell then went on to develop mathematical equations for them. These equations today are the foundation of electromagnetic study. Maxwell's equations explained the controversial "action at a distance" concept accepted by Newton and demonstrably true for gravitational, electrical and magnetic occurrences; but they explained such action in terms of fields.

Faraday's preoccupation with his idea of fields led him again and again to assert that gravitation, magnetism, electricity and light were at bottom one and the same thing. He made the then radical statement "The view I am so bold as to put forth considers, therefore, radiation (light) as a high species of vibration in the lines of force which are known to connect particles and also masses of matter together. It endeavors to dismiss the aether, but not the vibrations."

Maxwell's equations predicted the existence of electromagnetic waves or vibrations but it was not until many years later that Heinrich Hertz, a German schoolmaster, produced the first transmission and detection of these waves through the atmosphere, an experiment that was to produce radio transmission and the realization that light itself was an electromagnetic phenomenon.

During the years between 1822 and 1831, an American scientist and experimenter, Joseph Henry, was working with electricity and magnetism. But Henry worked long hours as a schoolmaster and the only time he had for experiment was during the brief summer holidays of those times (about one month elapsing between the end of one session and the beginning of the next) and whenever he found time at night. At the Albany Academy, in Albany, N. Y., Henry converted a room for experiment during the brief recesses and produced the same results from his examination of the interaction of electricity and magnetism. But Henry was not in contact with any scientific society. He was merely a schoolmaster in a provincial town, in a provincial country. He dared not publish his findings until he had gathered such a mass of data that its authority would make up for his own lack of stature in the scientific world. Unfortunately Henry waited too long and the truth came to him when he read of Faraday's revelations in a scientific journal. They paralleled his own investigations.

Henry eventually went to England and met Faraday and other renowned scientists who at first regarded him as a provincial pretender to knowledge. They soon realized that Joseph Henry was a scientist of the first rank and he found acceptance and acclaim with his discovery of other electrical principles.

As a result of his work, Faraday was elected to the Royal Society and his work was by no means confined to electromagnetism. His lifelong interest in chemistry continued. With Davy he had pursued answers to many questions in chemistry. Later, on his own, he made a study of chlorine and in the process discovered new chlorides of carbon. He studied the diffusion of gases and managed to liquefy gases. In studying the passage of electrical currents through solutions of chemicals, he developed the special branch of physics and chemistry called electrochemistry. Today Faraday's Laws of Electrolysis state exact relationships between chemical particles in a solution and the electric current required to deposit them on a metal plate.

Even in his own lifetime Faraday saw his discoveries being put to use by commerce and industry. Faraday and his wife had long lived on the edge of poverty. At the time of his great discovery of electromagnetic rules of behavior, he was making about £100 a year. He cheerfully accepted the poverty and wanted only to be left alone to experiment. But as his fame grew, industry called on him to help solve many practical problems. In 1830 his income from such consultation was about

£1,000. Friends assured him that if he continued to work with industry he would surely reach £5,000 within a year or two. But Faraday's passion was the laboratory and he found that industry, however rewarding it might be economically, was robbing him of precious time. He deliberately turned his back on a comfortable income, returning to his laboratory and the research he loved. He worked there in a tattered apron, his mind filled with thousands of schemes and ideas. Many of them did not work but Faraday declared he would be satisfied if only one experiment in a thousand produced useful results.

Faraday's early habit of self-education turned him into one of the most popular lecturers the Royal Society ever had. He worked hard to present his material efficiently and, if possible, with dramatization. He reportedly once threw a coal scuttle, a poker and a pair of tongs at the large permanent magnet in the lecture hall. When they all stuck fast, he had amply demonstrated the force of magnetic attraction. A "Faraday lecture" was always well attended, frequently by royalty and on several occasions by the novelist Charles Dickens. Dickens was so taken with Faraday's lectures he asked if he could report them in a magazine he was editing. Faraday agreed. He even began a series of lectures for children on the principles of science and added an evening lecture each week for interested adults.

As his fame and popularity grew, Faraday was urged frequently to accept the presidency of the Royal Society but he always refused. He had come from a plain background and he did not aspire to high office of any sort. He wanted to remain merely Michael Faraday and to continue his researches. Poverty he had fortunately left behind. He had been named Fullerian professor of chemistry for the remainder of his life. Queen Victoria gave him a house in which to live. Honors came to him from all over the world.

During the last years of his life, his memory began to fail. He was watched over by his niece. Knowing he could not complete work he had undertaken, Faraday freely gave his work to others so they might complete it for the benefit of science, his lifelong mistress. He died on August 26, 1867.

It is very difficult to imagine what our life would be like today without the discoveries of Faraday. While it may well be argued that if Faraday had not discovered so many electromagnetic principles someone else would, Faraday is the man to whom the honor belongs.

Uncounted millions of electric motors help do the world's work—because Faraday discovered that the flow of electrons in a wire can create magnetic force, and that force can be put to work. Great generators of electricity supply light and power to cities—because Faraday discovered that a copper wire moving through a magnetic field could produce a current of electricity. All these results are the harvest of Faraday's passion to understand the relationship between electricity and magnetism.

At the time Faraday's work was what we today call "pure" research—that is, research with no practical application in view. This love of pure science frequently is scorned by industrialists and practical, worldly men. It was so in Faraday's time also. On one occasion the Duke of Wellington suggested to Faraday that he become interested in a more "practical" line of research. Fortunately for us, Faraday refused the suggestion.

Joseph Lister: Antiseptic Surgery

We live today in a puncture-proof world. No matter how many square inches of our skin are scraped, torn, pierced or cut we can, with the simple application of an antiseptic and a bandage, go about our business with only minor discomfort. Only in the most severe cases is it necessary to enter a hospital because of broken or torn epidermis. Even if infection has begun, we have powerful germ killers at our command that can quickly cleanse the entire bloodstream. For specific germs we have specific remedies. The hospitals we enter from time to time are places of healing; they are clean, well ordered and maintained. We think of these hospitals as places where healing can occur, where health can be restored.

Yet not so many years ago, hospitals were places of death. Doctors of the middle nineteenth century preferred to treat patients—even to the extent of operating on them—in their homes. For hospitals were dangerous places. To enter one, and to be operated on, however successfully, was frequently to be dead within a week. The saying that "the operation was successful but the patient died" literally was true. For in the hospitals of a hundred years ago, and less than a hundred years ago, postoperative infection was the rule rather than the exception. And there was absolutely nothing anyone could do about it. For some reason, then unknown, the mortality rate in hospitals was higher than that of patients treated at home. So hospitals themselves, dedicated to curing people, were apparently sources of death.

Singlehandedly, one man changed the entire outlook on hospital care and the treatment of surgical cases. His name was Joseph Lister.

Through years of effort, Joseph Lister convinced the medical profession throughout the world that the germ theory of disease and infection was correct. He developed the first successful method of attacking germs in wounds caused by operations or accidents. By doing this he opened the way for successful surgery on parts of the body that surgeons had never dared touch for fear of inviting infection. He developed absorbent ligatures for tying internal structures together, proving finally that the body itself, with its own recuperative powers, would adjust to the presence of a foreign substance in the body, would in some cases dissolve or protectively coat such objects so they would cause no harm. Through his work the life span of every generation following him has been prolonged.

A glimpse into yesterday's best-run hospitals would be more terrifying for us today than any horror film developed by Hollywood.

The first thing that would greet you on stepping through the entrance of such a hospital would be the smell. Like a gray wave, the stench of rotting human flesh would roll over you and unquestionably you would be ill on the spot. In the wards, crowded with patients who had little chance to live, would be men with rotting arms, hands, feet, legs, necks. You would not have to be a surgeon to know something was wrong. For even if the smell did not exist, a glance at the swollen red, purple, gray areas surrounding bandages would convince you that these patients had very little chance to survive.

As you passed the operating room, your ears would be

assaulted by shrieks and screams of agony coming from the mouths of the patients being operated on—for there was no anesthesia when Joseph Lister began his study of medicine. Male nurses were required in the operating rooms and they had to be large and strong. Among their duties was that of holding the patient down on the operating table. After each operation, they sprinkled a few handfuls of sawdust on the blood-soaked floors of the rooms and mopped them out— hastily because the moment an operation was completed the next patient came to be "cured."

Surgeons of that day were accustomed to the sights, sounds and smells of the operating room and the wards. They, in fact, prided themselves on their ability to "take it," as we would say today. An observer from today's world would probably call them calloused men. They ignored the screams while they operated, they accepted the dread "hospital diseases," as they were called, which usually set in after an operation, and they discussed among themselves without showing any emotion the poor chance for survival. They were forced to do all this by the circumstances. The best surgeons were those who could perform an operation the fastest—for the less time the wound was exposed to the hospital atmosphere, the better were the patient's chances for survival. Many a skilled surgeon would make an incision, tie off a broken artery or set a fractured bone and sew up the wound within two minutes.

As a symbol of their skill, they wore the same apron at each operation for as long as a year: encrusted with the blood of many patients and all the filth of operations.

Among the hospital diseases the greatest killers were what then were called septicemia, pyemia, erysipelas, tetanus and hospital gangrene. Another cause of postoperative death was secondary hemorrhage when ligatures were removed from healing wounds. Periodically mysterious epidemics of the "hospital diseases" swept through the wards, killing patients in wholesale lots. The mortality rate of amputation surgery was normally one in three, but when the epidemics struck, patients who were recovering from such operations sickened and died. In many such instances all the patients in a ward died. When that happened, the ward was locked and left vacant for an extended period of time, until the hospital officials felt the epidemic had passed.

The best surgeons of that day refused to operate within the peritoneum, which is the membrane enclosing the stomach and intestines and other internal organs. An incision there, they had learned from experience, meant certain death. Since many tumors and abscesses formed within this membrane, such patients admitted to the hospital were made as comfortable as possible until they inevitably died.

And hospital comfort then was not what it is now. Bed linens went unchanged for weeks. Floors were rarely scrubbed and ventilation was practically nonexistent. The result was a room full of sick and dying people in filth they could not avoid. Nurses were difficult to get and the women who served as such aides were those to whom such horror and dirt were nothing unusual.

Our judgment today of such hospitals would be harsh, and criticism of medical knowledge of that time scathing. But progress in all fields of human knowledge has been slow and the history of medical progress follows the usual pattern.

From prehistoric times men have tried to fight illness, disease and avoidable death. Early in man's existence the presence of illness or disease was attributed to divine displeasure or the temporary ascendency of gods of evil. From these beliefs rose the priest-physicians who combined religious ceremony with medical practice. We smile today at vestigial evidence of this among primitive tribes where the witch doctor still functions, but all tribes everywhere in earliest history had some form of the mixture of religion and medicine.

Even when Greek civilization was at its height, divine intervention was sought to overcome illness. In Biblical times the demons of disease were exorcised to promote health. As Greek scholars turned to science they began observing illness a little more closely and attributed some forms of disease to what were termed "miasmas." A miasma is defined today as "a noxious effluvium formerly supposed to emanate from putrescent matter, swamps, etc., and to float in the air, especially in night mists."

From this idea of the source of disease we still have, among uneducated people, some who resolutely close their windows at night reasoning that "night air is bad"—and damp night air worse, being the cause of colds. This thought can also be traced to the idea that sitting in drafts is a cause of colds. That the idea is false does nothing to help it die out among millions of resolute parents trying to protect their young from the troublesome common cold.

The idea, however, that there was "something" in the air that caused disease had an element of truth in it. In Joseph Lister's time doctors believed that the "something" was oxygen itself, that the very life-giving element had a corrupting or disease-causing aspect and consequently such diseases of the hospital as gangrene and other forms of tissue and blood poisoning were unavoidable. None asked themselves why, if this were true, such diseases were less likely to strike a patient at home than in the hospital—for surely there was as much oxygen in the air at home as in the wards.

The surgeons did not even suspect that their symbols of experience and competence—their blood and pus-covered aprons

—were carriers of disease. Many surgeons, in their skillful haste to complete an operation, had ligatures already threaded on rusty steel needles before beginning the incision. To have them placed handily, they were stuck in the front of their filthy aprons from which the surgeons could pluck them when the time came to sew up the patient's wound, thus insuring infection if, by chance, the patient had escaped it until then.

In such an atmosphere young Joseph Lister began his medical career.

Joseph Lister was born in 1827 in Upton, England, the son of well-to-do Quaker parents. Quiet, reserved and sensitive, yet with a deep-seated stubbornness about him, he at one time considered the study of botany. His own and his family's religious beliefs precluded his entering certain professions. But medicine was open to him and he enrolled as a student in the London University College Hospital, where he undertook the course in surgery. He wore the plain dress of Quakers and his conversation abounded with "thee's" and "thou's." He was liked by his fellow students but remained outside their daily orbits since he could not join them in taverns or at parties.

Lister's manner and temperament did not seem to suit the rough-and-ready world of surgery of that time. He was visibly pained by other people's pain; he rarely could enter a ward without wincing at the prevalent conditions—but he studied and worked with intensity. And he asked questions. He was never, even as a student, convinced that the hospital diseases could not be abolished. In 1846 he witnessed an operation where the newly discovered anesthetic, ether, was used. The value of ether as an anesthetic had been discovered by an American dentist, Dr. Horace Wells, and the results of its use astonished the medical world. For the first time in history, a patient could undergo surgery without feeling the pain of the knife. It also, as Lister noted, eliminated the need for speed in operating, at least so far as hurting the patient was concerned. As a student, Lister doubted the widely held belief that oxygen caused the hospital diseases, and he felt even then that anesthesia gave the surgeon time: time to observe the condition of the patient's wound or trouble; time to study the health of the tissues; time, above all, to clean instruments, clean the wound and let no foreign matter enter during operation. But his questions asked of his friendly superiors brought only looks of incredulity and mild reproof. If it is not oxygen that causes the diseases, then what is it? he was asked. And at that time he had no answers.

When he graduated from the University Hospital he already had begun research on the health of tissues. His approach was simple: study bits of unhealthy tissue and try to discover or deduce what made them unhealthy. He spent endless nights peering through his microscope at prepared slides of all manner of diseased tissues. On one occasion he saw, or thought he saw, a swarm of microscopic bits of life moving back and forth through the septic liquid from a bit of tissue. But he was unable to find them again for many years.

Lister's obvious intelligence and talent for research led to the suggestion that he visit famous surgeons throughout Europe to observe their methods and talk with them about hospital diseases. His mentor at the University College Hospital, Professor William Sharpey, suggested that he could do no better anywhere than go to Edinburgh and watch the famous surgeon, James Syme, at work. William Sharpey wrote ahead to his friend Syme and when Lister arrived he made a markedly good impression on the famous surgeon. Syme persuaded Lister to stay on under him, which he did, and he eventually married James Syme's daughter Agnes. Between lectures and work in the operating room, Lister continued his research, stubbornly trying to find the cause or causes of hospital diseases. He experimented on frogs and bats to discover what actually took place when tissues became inflamed. He searched for the cause of blood clotting. With the help of his wife, he read all foreign medical journals searching for more and more information on hospital diseases. But everywhere he turned Lister found more ignorance than truth on the matter that interested him most.

In 1860 he accepted the post of teacher of surgery at the University of Glasgow. As all such teachers did, he worked in the medical college and had a hospital ward of post-surgery patients under his care. Conditions in his ward when he first arrived were, if anything, worse than in similar hospitals throughout the British Isles. Armed now with the authority of a position, Lister demanded that his ward be cleansed thoroughly and that bed sheets be changed regularly and the ward ventilated. But when the nurse reluctantly threw open the windows to get the "surgical smell" out, an overpowering tide of it rolled in. Lister looked outside and saw nothing but the drab "back yard" of industrial Glasgow. He asked what caused the odor from outside and the nurse shrugged and said that she didn't know, the stench had been there for the past several years.

Uninformed and relatively unhappy about that situation, Lister did the best he could for the patients in his ward. Many had gangrene and many died, but some lived. It was the accepted situation and, save for the unaccountable stench from outside, Lister was simply in another hospital. But it was here, in this ward in Glasgow, that Lister's first steps to eradicate hospital diseases were to meet with success.

For five years Lister pursued his work at the hospital and

among his students while continuing his researches at night. His wife was also interested in the problem of medicine and surgery and she gave him great assistance. But all their combined reading and discussion proved fruitless. Lister, by then, had established his clean ward and forced the hospital manager to accept the additional cost it entailed, but he met with the ridicule and contempt of his colleagues, who saw no difference between Lister's clean, well-lighted ward and their own filthy ones.

Then, in 1865, Lister's attention was drawn to an article in the periodical published by the French Scientific Academy. It was not a medical article; it dealt with chemistry, specifically with organic chemistry and the chemist's explanation of the fermentation of wine and the spoilage of milk. Lister read the article with intense interest and when he grasped fully what had been revealed to him, he knew that the door had swung wide open. He knew the answer to hospital diseases. The chemist who had conducted the experiments with the wine and milk was Louis Pasteur.

Born in 1822, Louis Pasteur had been trained as a chemist. In temperament he was nearly the opposite of Lister: voluble, quick-tempered, and unconcerned about the opinions of his colleagues. In one respect, however, the two men were alike. Both had an inexhaustible store of stubbornness to use on the solution of problems.

Early in his career Pasteur became interested in studying organisms visible only under the microscope, or microorganisms. In his studies he came in conflict with several accepted theories of his time, one of which was of great importance. Strange as it may seem to us today, many scientists of Pasteur's time believed that small examples of animate life could arise spontaneously from inorganic matter; thus caterpillars were "born spontaneously" from leaves and leaf mold. What was little understood in those days was the life cycle of numerous animals. The metamorphosis of such creatures as moths and butterflies was not understood. Consequently the true origin of caterpillars—developing from eggs laid by moths and butterflies—remained hidden.

In one famous experiment designed to prove that life could be produced spontaneously, John Needham, a scientist of the eighteenth century, boiled meat gravy and placed it in corked flasks. Within a few days there was evidence of bacteriological growth in the solution. Since Needham believed he had killed all life by boiling the liquid, he held that the existence of the bacteria proved life could spring from inanimate matter. At the time it was very convincing. But what he and others neglected in the carefully conducted experiment was the very air surrounding them and the apparatus. The boiled gravy, when placed in flasks, did not fill the flasks. Air was permitted to enter and was corked with the test solution. And there are, as we know now, bacteria present in all samples of air except those thoroughly sterilized or taken at high altitudes or latitudes.

Pasteur suspected that the atmosphere carried bacteria in it and repeated Needham's experiment with one difference. He drew out the necks of his flasks in an elongated bent shape much like the sinktrap below a sink. When he boiled his solutions, steam drove out all the air in the neck of the flask and condensing moisture in the trap literally "trapped" bacteria that tried to enter when the flask was cooled. In this way Pasteur kept his solution free from bacteria, and from his results could state that life must spring from life, not from inanimate matter.

The paper Pasteur wrote and that Lister read with such great excitement concerned his studies in the fermentation of wine and phenomenon of milk turning sour. He examined many samples of wine that had not fermented in the approved manner but had gone on and become vinegar. In this wine he discovered unusual bacteria from diseased grapes. His solution foreshadowed the process known by his name today: pasteurization. He heated new wine samples for a prolonged period but kept them below the boiling point of alcohol and then put the wine into flasks. To control his experiment he placed untreated wine in other flasks and the two sets were left for ten months. On opening the flasks, tasters found the treated wine was in good condition while the untreated wine had gone bad.

Pasteur himself came to believe that if bacteria could cause disease among plants, it could cause disease in men. Much of his later career was devoted to this theory and to the development of vaccinations to prevent epidemic and troublesome diseases. Since he was not a surgeon and not acquainted with hospital problems, he did not see what Lister immediately perceived on reading the paper on wine fermentation: that bacteria in the air entered wounds and produced the dreaded gangrene and other types of tissue and blood poisoning.

Lister set to work immediately and duplicated Pasteur's experiments successfully. Next he examined fermenting solutions under his microscope and actually saw the "germs" swarming and multiplying in the warm, favorable liquids. After a great deal of searching, he finally saw the germs in diseased blood and serum from his patients. There, too, they were swarming and multiplying.

His next step was to find something to kill the germs. Pasteur had heated his solutions to eradicate the bacteria but this was a course Lister could not follow with his patients. Pasteur also had discovered that many bacteria could be eliminated from a liquid by filtering. Lister could not do that. He realized he must find an antiseptic, one that would not harm the patient but which would be of sufficient strength to kill the germs. According to one report, he discovered his first antiseptic while reading the newspaper account of city officials who had used carbolic acid to eliminate the stench of a garbage dump. They reported that the odor was removed by the acid. Lister suspected that the germs in the poisoned tissues of the patients accounted for the nauseating odor that pervaded the wards, and he decided to try carbolic acid.

At first he used it full strength on a patient with a compound bone fracture. Fractures were frequent in the early days of industrial machinery development, and often resulted in gangrene because patients who suffered such breaks usually were admitted to the hospital with grime and soot and grease already embedded in the wound.

His first effort to use carbolic failed because the patient, who had a large open wound on one leg, had remained at home without treatment for several days after his accident. Whoever this nameless person was, he apparently knew of the high mortality rate in the hospital and had decided to take his chances away from medical care. The result was that gangrene already had entered the wound and his body before Lister got to him. The man died the night he was admitted.

A few days later a young boy with a broken leg was carried into the hospital. There was a small, relatively clean break of the skin, and Lister immediately dipped a piece of lint in carbolic acid and spread it over the wound. He placed a second piece of lint over the first so that it completely covered the torn skin, isolating it from the air. Then he took the boy to the operating room and set the bones of his leg. But he gave strict orders that under no circumstances was the bandage to be lifted from the wound. As the bandages dried, more acid was dripped onto the lint.

Infection usually was evident within four days following an accident, and as the hours and days and nights passed, Lister kept careful watch over the boy. When at last Lister felt the danger was past, he lifted the lint and inspected the broken skin. Though slightly red from acid burn, it was growing over, healing itself with none of the odor or the appearance of putrefaction.

A young assistant of Lister, Hector Cameron, had been torn between loyalty and doubt about his superior's theory and procedure, but when he saw that healing wound he knew—as Lister had confidently assumed beforehand—that a cure for hospital diseases at last had been found.

Lister searched endlessly for more effective bandages and tried tinfoil, a putty mixture, calico and silk cloths until he found the one best suited to retain the acid. He experimented with various strengths of solutions of carbolic as well as other antiseptics.

Very soon he learned that to insure successful healing he had literally to wash all the damaged tissues with antiseptic before placing the bandage over the wound. Days and weeks and months went by and the mortality rate in Lister's ward dropped until for a long period of time he lost no patients from gangrene or blood poisoning.

This was all the more astonishing when the cause of the peculiar odor from outside the hospital was discovered. Workmen just outside his ward excavated near the foundation of the hospital, thinking that the probable cause was a stopped drain. To everyone's horror, the men's shovels uncovered rows of coffins buried only inches below the surface of the ground. In them were bodies of people who had died in a cholera epidemic in 1849. Through some quirk of soil condition and moisture, the corpses were almost perfectly preserved and had not decomposed.

Lister had been seeking to banish disease while working with patients only a few feet away from a most deadly source of it. Yet for the nine months prior to the discovery of these bodies, not one case of gangrene or blood poisoning had appeared in his ward.

Lister believed he had absolute proof of the effectiveness of his antiseptic method of treatment. Without his knowing it, he was working in as unhealthy an atmosphere as he could possibly have chosen; the ward across the hall—a scant twelve feet away—continued to have the high incidence of disease and death common to all the world's hospital wards, had in fact had to be closed because of an epidemic. Yet his ward had no deaths from diseases.

As his self-taught skill and knowledge of antiseptics increased, Lister became more confident and successfully operated on patients where all others had failed. He became interested in the problem of tying off broken arteries with ligatures. Until he experimented, the common practice was to tie the blood vessel with a silk ligature and leave one end of it long and hanging from the wound, which was stitched together with silver wire. At some point in the healing process, the surgeon returned and tried to draw out the silk twine. Frequently the result was a hemorrhage within the body of the patient.

Lister observed that broken bone fragments left in a wound caused no eventual trouble, that somehow the body managed to live with them or to absorb them, and it occurred to him that a ligature could safely be left within the body. The trouble with most of the silk ligatures—like all other surgical equipment— was that they were not sterile when used. The fibers of silk could and did secrete many germs which automatically insured disease when put to use. Lister decided to experiment but he did not want to work first on a human patient.

He selected an aging horse at the veterinary college and tied the left carotid artery with a short piece of silk which was saturated in carbolic acid. He then closed the wound, leaving the ligature inside. Six weeks later the horse died of old age, and although Lister himself was ill at the time, his assistant, Hector Cameron, cut out the side of the horse's neck and took it quickly to Lister's home. Despite a heavy cold, Lister was up, dressed and eager to examine the results of his experiment. Until 2 A.M. he studied the tissues and the remainder of the silk ligature. There had been no infection and the living tissue of the horse had begun to coat and absorb the silk.

Shortly after this experiment he was asked to heal an elderly woman who was suffering from aneurysm of the common femoral artery. He used a short silk ligature, soaked, needless to say, in carbolic acid. The wound healed quickly and when she died a year later from other causes, Lister asked and was granted permission to examine the artery where he had tied it. The silk ligature was very much present still and Lister was disappointed. He was looking for total absorption of the ligature by the living tissues of the patient. He turned next to catgut and tried it on a young calf. After a month, he had the calf killed and examined the ligatures carefully. Though they still retained their original form and color, he saw—after a first shock of disappointment—that living tissues coated the ligatures and that they were in the process of being assimilated.

Throughout all his experimenting, Lister taught his students and served the patients in his ward, day and night. He knew he had the means to wipe out hospital diseases forever. Further, with his method, operations could be performed that surgeons had not dared to try before. Human life could be prolonged and the high mortality rate associated with hospitals could be greatly reduced.

On several occasions while still at Glasgow he tried to interest his fellow surgeons in his method. But the surgeon in Ward 23, across from his disease-free ward, ridiculed Lister's "germ" theory. The few who showed interest got the mistaken idea that it was the carbolic acid that affected the cure. They couldn't grasp the idea of germs floating about in the air—and Pasteur, who was he?

For months his father-in-law, Dr. Syme, had been urging Lister to publish the astonishing results of his antiseptic theory, but Lister had felt he could not do so until he had perfected bandages, ligatures and antiseptic solutions beyond their present state. He did write a paper which was published in *Lancet,* a medical publication, but he emphasized the aspect of treating compound fractures and did not make the paper as specific about his antiseptic system as he should have. Inquiries from medical men throughout Britain showed they could not—or would not—grasp the idea of germs, microorganisms being at the root of disease—whether cholera, bubonic plague or gangrene.

His next chance to expound his theory came when he was asked to speak at a British Medical Association meeting in Dublin. The year was 1867. In carefully chosen words he told the assembled surgeons and physicians what he had proved, what he had done and what his system could do for medicine throughout the world.

When he had finished a few doctors asked questions, but Lister had the uneasy feeling that there was great hostility to what he had said. He could not fathom it. Why would doctors, dedicated to healing, turn their backs on a method that had proven itself—that they could try certainly with at least no more harmful effects than the methods they were using?

What Lister, and many men like him, forgot was that to the average mind—of a doctor or anyone else—the idea of radical change from an habitual course of action is the most frightening, repellent thing imaginable. It mattered to those doctors not at all that there just might be something in what Lister was saying.

One doctor rose at that meeting and derided the idea of germs, rejecting Pasteur's proof of their existence. Here, Lister was beginning to learn with astonishment, were no scientists, medical or otherwise. Here were comfortable, well-fed, contented, middle-aged men who would not give any consideration to something so "subversive" as germs or Lister or any experiments. Lister began to suspect that the epithet his wife's father used might be correct. Fools, was the word.

In 1869 Joseph Lister applied for the position of Clinical Surgeon at Edinburgh University. James Syme, in ill health, was retiring. During his last weeks in Glasgow he began to write a lengthy article that explained his antiseptic surgery in great detail and when it was finished he sent it to the journal that had printed his first paper on the subject, *Lancet*. The title was "On the Effects of the Antiseptic System of Treatment upon the Salubrity of a Surgical Hospital."

In his long article, which was serialized in *Lancet,* Lister piled detail on detail, fact on fact in this one great effort to find acceptance for his method. He pointed out that the Glasgow Hospital where he had discovered and practiced his method had, since it was built, shown a higher rate of disease than other hospitals and that the ground floor wards—of which his male ward was one—were most seriously affected by the discovered cholera victims. Yet that for a period of over three years, using

his method, there were no postoperative deaths from gangrene
or blood poisoning.

In reply to his article, the Secretary of the Royal Infirmary
in Glasgow sent a letter which *Lancet* also published. In it the
Secretary said, "In their opinion, which is shared by a number
belonging to the medical profession, the improved health and
satisfactory condition of the hospital, which has been as marked
in the medical as in the surgical department, is mainly attribu-
table to the better ventilation, the improved dietary and the
excellent nursing to which the Directors have given so much
attention in late years."

Lister replied, again setting forth his data which no one would
believe. In following issues of *Lancet* various doctors wrote in
saying that they had tried Lister's "carbolic acid treatment"
with little success. But these men, like many others, did not
employ carbolic as Lister did. In one reported instance, twelve
hours elapsed between the operation and the application of
carbolic acid. Naturally, during that time, germs entered the
wound and it became infected.

Lister's next great rebuff came at another meeting of the
British Medical Society where his germ theory and his antiseptic method were publicly attacked by the speaker on surgery,
a Mr. Thomas Nunneley. Lister sat near the front of the
auditorium, stunned by the embarrassment, surrounded principally by surgeons and physicians who favored the speaker's
attack. Following the speech, which amounted to official re-
jection of the germ theory and antiseptics, others rose and
supported the attacker. One man reportedly accused Lister of
unethical, if not criminal, action in his use of carbolic acid and
the methods of surgery he was successfully employing—for by
this time Lister had dared to operate on large internal abscesses
and once had opened the adominal wall to operate on an

extremely bad hernia. In both cases—and in others like them—the patients recovered easily. But this did not stop his accusers. They always relied on the chance factor, claiming that Lister had been lucky.

Lister returned to Edinburgh from that meeting and quite understandably began to erect defenses against the stinging criticism he had received and would continue to receive. He filled his days and nights with work. His students admired him and he taught them his theory. His patients recovered, as usual, without infection and his research went on. But even the editor of the *Lancet* turned against him. When derogatory letters failed to come into the editorial office to be printed, the magazine ran editorials denouncing Lister's method.

Until he was nearly fifty, Lister worked on in Edinburgh outwardly calm and actually, in many ways, quite happy. But he hated to lose the fight to convince his colleagues of the existence of germs. By personal contact with some surgeons he had a few converts. But still the overwhelming number of practicing doctors rejected him.

He finally startled his wife by announcing he wanted to leave Edinburgh and take a post in a London hospital. Since London surgeons had proved to be among the most hostile to him, his wife could not understand his motives. But they were formed precisely because of the hostility of London to his methods.

Then, as now, a patient was allowed to select the surgeon who would perform whatever operation was demanded, and when Lister finally got a post in small King's College Hospital he found time hanging heavily on his hands: no patients wanted to be treated by Lister. More to the point, physicians who first saw patients routed them away from Lister. His small ward of only about twenty-five beds remained empty. His students, of which he had about seventy instead of nearly ten times that number in Edinburgh, were polite enough but they let it be known that they were having no germ theory with their medical training.

Unquestionably the first weeks in London were the most discouraging that Lister had to face. In Edinburgh, at least, he had enthusiastic students and many friends. In London he was very nearly alone.

Yet during those years of unacceptance in Britain, Lister was being accepted on the continent of Europe. First a Danish surgeon, Dr. Mathias Saxtorph, Professor of Surgery at the University of Copenhagen, tried and approved Lister's methods. Next, Dr. von Nussbaum of Munich, Germany, saw the light and published a paper praising Lister's method. Then Dr. Richard von Volkmann, Professor of Surgery at Halle, Germany, joined the ranks. His case was particularly outstanding since Germany was in the midst of the Franco-Prussian War and the battlefield casualties made a shambles of hospitals in the warring lands. Dr. von Volkmann had been on the verge of closing one hospital when, in desperation, he tried Lister's method. He, too, gave unrestrained praise to Lister.

Europe, it seemed, was not quite so backward about trying something new as was Britain. Soon surgeons from all over Europe were writing of the amazing results obtained by the use of Lister's method.

Doctors in King's College Hospital in London continued to ignore Lister, and one who did the most ignoring was a John Wood, who had hoped to get the post Lister got.

Lister's first patient in London was a man who had broken his kneecap. The only reason he sought out Lister was that the other wards in the hospital were full. Ordinarily a broken kneecap was treated by simply letting the broken bones knit of themselves without setting. Lister decided to operate. He opened the joint and wired the bones together—after cleaning the wound—and placing a carbolic acid bandage on it. Lister knew the man would recover but it was the first evidence his colleagues had of the use of antiseptics and many felt Lister should be reprimanded for even attempting the operation. His next patient was a man whose case had been given up as hopeless and when Lister operated successfully on him and the man was on his way to complete recovery, Wood came into Lister's ward. He fully expected the man to die. When he saw the patient was on the road to being well, his reserve and enmity vanished. He called in others of the hospital staff and had them look at Lister's patient. They too began dimly to see that Lister very definitely knew something that they did not.

From that moment on, Lister's work was made much easier. Instead of hostility he now found surgeons eager to understand his theory and his methods. Year by year the number of delicate operations increased and the mortality rates went down. Hospital after hospital adopted Lister's practice, and as the last decade of the nineteenth century began, hospital diseases became a thing of the past.

Further development and experiment by surgeons the world around produced eventually what we today call aseptic surgery. Instead of using quantities of antiseptic in operating rooms, surgeons began cleaning the rooms, the instruments, the hospital gowns and the patient before operating. In the germ-free atmosphere that resulted, operations could proceed without fear of infection.

Joseph Lister lived to see his method and Pasteur's theory accepted throughout the world. Honors came to the aging surgeon in overwhelming numbers. But the greatest was the increase in life span of the human race which, in hospital surgery, he had helped produce.

James Watt: Geni of Power

More than six thousand years ago an event took place that moved mankind a great distance away from savagery and toward civilization. Precisely when it occurred and exactly who was present, we will never know. But someone in that distant past, exhausted by his labors, looped a vine or a leather thong about the horns of one of his domesticated cattle and tied the ends to his crude wooden plow. Man had discovered a way to use energy other than his own to accomplish a task.

From that time forward, man searched for ways to use the energy of nature to do his work. He found that wind could propel his ships and turn the windmills he ingeniously built. He found that water plunging down a stream could turn a water wheel and grind grain. He learned to use other animals such as the horse, the donkey and the dog—and in times of slavery he used the muscles of his fellow men. Yet even free men found they had to exert themselves continuously doing a thousand tasks which today are accomplished by power-driven machinery.

It is remarkable that throughout man's history he has developed machines, political and social organizations and cultures of a very complex nature but until a little more than two hundred years ago he had not learned to exploit the power of nature to do his work for him on any large scale. As late as the latter half of the eighteenth century, man still was dependent on wind to propel ships, on horses and cattle to transport him and his goods and plow his fields. Water wheels that turned millstones were common throughout colonial America and all over the world.

The need for power was becoming more pressing and scientists and engineers everywhere recognized the need. As population grew in the countries of Europe the problem of feeding and clothing people put great strains on the ability of animals and men alike to produce the food and cloth—for there is a very real limit to the amount of work a man or a horse can accomplish without dropping dead from exhaustion.

As early as the seventeenth century men had tried to develop a source of power but they had met with indifferent success. The search, however, continued and during the latter half of the eighteenth century, James Watt, a Scotsman, joined in the common search. Through his efforts, more than those of any other man, a source of power was given the world, power that would run machines in factories, power that would propel ships and eventually drive trains. James Watt's practical steam engine ushered in the Industrial Revolution. It permitted cheap manufacture and took the centuries-long curse of exhausting physical labor from the back of the human race.

James Watt was born January 19, 1736, in Greenock, Scotland. He was the fourth of five children—three of whom died in infancy. James himself (very like Isaac Newton before him) was sickly and underdeveloped. In his early years Watt was continually attacked by migraine headaches. He frequently missed school and would spend days in his father's carpentry shop watching the men work. His father showed him how to use tools and the young Watt became quite skilful at repairing or building whatever struck his fancy. At school his physical condition brought the expected bullying from larger, stronger boys and, in fact, his teachers reported Watt to be "mentally retarded."

Watt's grandfather, Thomas Watt, had been an educated man, coming originally from Aberdeenshire in northern Scotland and settling in Cartsdyke near Greenock. Thomas Watt was a mathematician, astronomer and navigator. He earned an excellent living teaching navigation in the small town on the banks of the Clyde estuary, which already was becoming a shipping center.

Watt's father, also named James, became a carpenter's apprentice and eventually moved to Greenock where he began a thriving business. He was not content to remain a mere carpenter and turned to building both houses and ships, employing many men and becoming a leading figure in the town, which then numbered a little over three thousand in population.

Watt, then, came from a background that held the two requirements for a successful engineer or inventor: technical knowledge of the fields of machinery and mathematics, plus skill in building articles either from wood or metal—for his father gave him a small forge and metal-working tools for his amusement while he was home from school nursing his recurrent migraine headaches. Later his father set up a workshop for his son in the attic of their home and here Watt worked by himself during his early teens.

Among the many untrue myths surrounding famous figures of the past is one connected with Watt. According to it, he got the idea for his steam engine by watching steam raise the lid of a teakettle on his mother's stove. Steam may have raised the teakettle lid. Watt may have observed it. But that is where the matter ended. He never connected such an observation to his research into steam power.

By all standards in Greenock—or any other small town in

Scotland—James Watt came from a well-to-do background. He could anticipate going to the best schools and colleges and could pursue any career he might have wished. But before he could even undertake such education or decide upon a career, his father began to suffer reverses in business. One by one the ideas of leading even a moderately luxurious life had to be abandoned. Then, when Watt was eighteen, his mother died. It became evident that the young man would have to "seek his fortune" on his own and he chose to go to Glasgow and apprentice himself to a scientific instrument maker.

The making of scientific instruments and the repair of them was an honorable enough career in those days for a young man without money, and Watt's early training in working metals and wood, plus his interest in mathematics and navigation, indicated this would be a good course to follow. Unfortunately, Glasgow had no instrument makers and Watt seemed to be frustrated in his efforts to get on his feet. A by-product of his decision to go to Glasgow, however, proved to be his salvation. His mother's people lived in Glascow and Watt stayed with them. They had many friends among the university professors, and one, Professor Robert Dick, took an interest in the young, shy and still rather sickly James Watt.

Dr. Dick was a professor of physics. He learned of Watt's ambitions and realized that the university could well use a trained instrument repairer and maker. He advised Watt to go to London and spend a year as an apprentice to such an instrument man and then return. This Watt managed to do and on his return to Glasgow was set up in the university. He had a room to live in and a workshop. Best of all he had the intellectual stimulation of working among well-trained minds, minds that were involved with the many problems of science and the engineering of his day.

At the age of twenty-one Watt began moving directly toward the problem of the steam engine and his solution of it. At first he had no inkling of this but in retrospect he knew that his inclusion in the university and his informal training in the major problems facing scientists of that day were the first steps toward greatness.

The Glasgow, and the Scotland, and the Britain of Watt's youth were in many ways as primitive as some sections of Asia and Africa today. Illiteracy was common. Life spans were short. Disease in the form of plagues periodically swept the land. Glasgow had no claim to distinction save the university. Scotland was a wilderness of heath and fen; towns and villages were connected, if at all, by "roads" that would break the wheels of any wagon or cart long before a journey between two settlements could be accomplished. Supplies came inland from seaports on horseback and long trains of horses were the usual sight on these roads.

A hint of the actual state of conditions comes in the journey Watt made from Glasgow to London. It contained all the perils that might face us today in planning a journey through remote Amazon jungles. The question arose as to whether it would be safer for Watt to travel by land or by sea. He could easily hire passage on one of the coastwise sailing ships and hope to reach London. But the seas surrounding Britain were alive with pirate vessels, and such a journey was by no means safe. Traveling by horseback, on the other hand, was equally hazardous: highwaymen lurked behind hedge and tree. Inns were far apart and it was not uncommon for innkeepers to rob their guests—or give assistance to others in doing so, for a share of the proceeds. London itself swarmed with thieves and murderers. What they missed, the "press gangs" frequently took. Press gangs operated to help supply crews to warships, merchant ships or colonial plantations. Any man befuddled by drink or merely walking alone along a narrow, dark street was likely to be seized and bound, slugged or doped and to wake up aboard some ship bound for the Mediterranean battles or a Carolina plantation. During Watt's stay in London the need for crews was great and papers of the day proudly pointed to the fact that in one night press gangs supplied a thousand men to serve, however unwillingly, aboard the ships of the British Navy.

There is little wonder that a young man of Watt's temperament found happy security within the walls of the University of Glasgow. It was sanctuary and laboratory all in one.

Britain at the time of Watt's early career was largely an agricultural country. In manufacturing, woolen goods exceeded the monetary value of all other products combined. But the woolen industry was still a piecework and handwork business. In fact, workers did their jobs in their own homes and took the spun, carded or woven wool to their employers for payment. Woolen goods were the chief export from Britain and the upstart cotton goods from the southern colonies in America had not yet gained a foothold. Iron was in demand for cannon and muskets, but in order to produce iron, the furnaces needed coal for fuel. By good chance, iron deposits in Britain were located near sources of coal. Without that happenstance Britain probably would have had to import finished iron goods. For if iron and coal deposits lay far apart, the cost of transporting coal by horseback to the ironworks would have put Britain's iron industry out of business.

The coal mines were worked regularly and their product was good. But as the mines were developed deeper and deeper into the earth, water frequently flooded them. Either those sinking a mine shaft were inadvertently digging a well, or the seepage from porous layers of underground soil soon filled the shafts and brought coal production to a halt. Many a businessman had been forced into bankruptcy by water which flooded his mines and this, of course, put miners out of work. This factor in the life of Britain was responsible for the search for a source of power to clear the mines of water, and it led Watt to join that search.

In his relationships with the professors at the University of Glasgow, Watt was more fortunate than he knew at the time. For Scotland, while being a poor and underdeveloped country, had a wealth of scholars and scientists. The universities of Glasgow and Edinburgh had men on their staffs and lecture schedules who were changing many fundamental ideas in science.

Air, for example, was not at all clearly understood by scientists of Watt's day. Nor was heat. And both of these were fundamental to Watt's development of the steam engine.

"Air" as it was thought of then is not what we know it is now. The word still retained the ancient Greek connotation, meaning that it was one of the Greek "elements"—earth, air, fire and water—of which all things presumably were composed. The fact that air had weight was scientifically proved by Evangelista Torricelli, a pupil of Galileo.

Torricelli's studies came about as a result of questions about water pumps in Galileo's day. One such pump was designed to lift water a distance of about forty feet and failed to do it. Galileo himself was asked why this was so, but the great Florentine scientist was either unable or unwilling to give an adequate reply. Water pumps of his time were similar to familiar hand pumps of today. They consisted of a tube or cylinder reaching to the water in the well and a piston fitted into the upper end of the cylinder. Upon moving the piston up and down, water is lifted because as the piston moves upward it creates a vacuum above the surface of the water in the cylinder. The usual answer to why water rises in the cylinder was that "nature abhors a vacuum," which was in keeping with Aristotle's thinking. But if this were so—and if it were all that was going on as the piston moved—then water should be able to be raised any desired height by simply pumping the piston indefinitely. To everyone's chagrin, continuous, frantic action of the piston would raise water no higher than about thirty feet. The reason, as Torricelli discovered, was that the water is not drawn up solely because of a vacuum above it, but because air pressure exerted on the surface of the liquid below pushed it up. Of course there had to be some vacuum—i.e. difference of pressure—for the water to move at all, but Torricelli's accomplishment was to show that the pressure exerted by air was sufficient only to support a column of water 34 feet above the free surface of the water in the well.

This information about air was known, of course, when Watt set to work, but it was about all that was known. Chemists realized air had to be present for most types of burning or combustion—the mystery of burning gunpowder in a vacuum remained unsolved. What chemists didn't know was the exact make-up of air as a mixture principally of two gases: nitrogen and oxygen. Experiments by Lavoisier and Priestley which identified oxygen were to come later in the eighteenth century. Nor did anyone know that oxygen frequently is in chemical combination with other elements, principally metals. Had they known this, they would have understood the mystery of gunpowder burning "without air," since the oxygen necessary for it to burn is in the compounds forming the gunpowder and is released when enough heat or pressure is applied.

Detailed knowledge of air and the pressure it exerts was not necessary, however, for inventors and other ingenious people to make use of it. The water pumps of Watt's day were substantially the same as those used in ancient Greek and Roman times. But they required either the muscle power of animals or people to make them work. And they certainly could not raise water from the bottoms of drowned mines deep in the earth. The water, of course, could have been lifted in stages, from one reservoir to another placed not more than thirty feet above it. But men would have had to pump continually, and even then they could not pump fast enough to clear the mineshafts.

Another area of concern to Watt was heat. But the theories of heat then being tried were far off the mark. Heat, like air, was considered to be, first of all, an element (earth, air, *fire* and water), then it was considered a particular substance called phlogiston. When flames were visible in the burning of a piece of wood, for example, it was believed the flames came from the phlogiston being somehow extracted from the wood. The fact that when the wood was totally burned there remained nothing but ashes weighing much less than the wood gave support to the idea the "something" had left the wood.

The phlogiston theory was widely held then and it was used to explain many otherwise baffling chemical changes. In turn, the phlogiston theory gave way to the idea that heat was an invisible fluid named "caloric," which mysteriously moved from warm objects to cooler ones. It was not until much later that heat was understood to be one of the basic forms of natural energy. We have retained a vestigial part of the invisible fluid theory in the measurement of heat energy today in the unit calorie which is fundamental in heat study. It is that quantity of heat energy necessary to raise one gram of water one degree centigrade.

Curiously, even as the caloric theory held sway, and the true nature of heat remained unrevealed to scientists, a teacher and friend of James Watt, Dr. Joseph Black, was making measurements of the heat required to do a variety of things. Among his experiments, which Watt later repeated himself, Black discovered that if you boiled water, the temperature of the boiling water remained unchanged during the process of turning the liquid to a vapor. The question, what was happening to the heat of the flame during the boiling process? naturally came to Black's mind. While he did not answer it as completely as we can today, he did learn that steam contained more heat energy than the boiling water. Black found that if he introduced only a very little steam to a vessel containing a generous amount of cold water, the temperature of the water was raised a great deal while a larger quantity of boiling water did not raise the cold water temperature as much.

During all these experiments Dr. Black was accepting the idea of the caloric fluid flowing from a hot body to a cold one. He established the method of measuring heat energy that we use today—and we still speak of heat flowing from a hot object to a cold one. In the process of conducting his experiments, Black determined, for the first time, what we call the latent heat of vaporization of water, which was to become important to Watt in his own work. Briefly, this idea of latent heat means that whereas it requires one calorie to raise the temperature of one gram of water one degree centigrade, it requires 540 calories to change one gram of water to one gram of steam. In turn this means that each gram of steam produced holds a tremendous amount of heat energy. When that steam is cooled and condensed again to water, the calories are "released" in the process. And if, as Watt was going to discover, the steam must be condensed for a steam engine to work, some practical way would have to be found to remove the heat from the steam.

Watt, Black and others who studied steam knew that when a gallon of water turns to steam, its volume increases about 1700 times. That is, the one gallon of water turns to 1700 gallons of steam if it is allowed to expand normally. Being a vapor, it can, of course, be compressed in containers or boilers, but early experiment showed that the force of expansion was not something that could be disregarded.

In a very large sense, Dr. Black was the first scientist to make precise measurements of heat energy. He placed the study of heat, as physicists would say, on a "quantitative basis." From the purely scientific point of view, this kind of measurement of largely unknown and as yet undefined physical phenomena is necessary before the thing being studied can be defined and its characteristics made clear. From the engineering point of view, however, the studies Black made were sufficient to permit the use of steam to operate an engine.

There was in fact a steam engine in use throughout England and parts of Europe when Watt began to work on the problem. And the potential power of steam had been known for centuries but not harnessed. Greek writings brought to Europe in the twelfth century show that a man named Hero had developed a crude little engine—more of a toy than anything else—that used steam. It was actually what we today call a reaction engine but it used steam to develop the thrust or force that produced motion. It consisted of a hollow sphere partially filled with water and pivoted on bearings so it could turn. From the sphere four tubes evenly arranged sprouted outward with their ends bent slightly all in the same direction. When a fire built beneath the sphere turned some of the water to steam it rushed out the nozzles, and like those of many water sprinklers today, produced a slight thrust which spun the sphere on its bearings. Hero was making use of the expansion of water as it turned to steam but that was all. No one thought then to build a large engine and try to connect it to a pump or wheel to turn a machine, but theoretically such a useful engine could have been constructed.

The first efforts to utilize steam to do useful work came early in the seventeenth century in England. Prior to those efforts, an Italian, Giovanni Battista della Porta, built a crude engine which, in his descriptions of it, did raise water "by means of fire," as the early experimenters put it. But so far as we know he did not develop his model engine and put it to use. Next a French landscape gardener, Salomon de Caus, used the ideas of the expansion of water turning to steam to produce special fountain effects. But in 1631 patents were granted in England to a Scotsman, David Ramsey, for a device which the inventor claimed would "Raise Water from Low Pits by Fire," make mills go and move ships against contrary winds and currents. What his actual machine was we do not know, for he never went beyond taking the patents. His application, however, shows that the problem of raising water from "pits" or mines or wells was even then acute enough to attract the interest and attention of inventors and, presumably, investors alike.

Edward Somerset, Marquis of Worcester, was a wealthy and tireless inventor who lived from 1601 to 1667. He studied the problem for many years and produced a "fire engine," as the early steam engines were called, that apparently did raise water to a height of forty feet—above the height that a normal hand pump would do which relied on atmospheric pressure and a partial vacuum created by the piston above the water in the tube or cylinder.

By this time certain elements of what was to be the modern

steam engine had been devised. A cylinder with a sliding piston was basic. Steam was admitted to a sealed portion of the cylinder below the piston, and this drove the piston upward. The cylinder in the early engine was arranged vertically for a particular reason. For when the piston had been driven upward, the steam that had forced it up was condensed and a partial vacuum was created below the piston. Then atmospheric pressure pushing on the other side of the piston would force it down. Steam again was admitted and the process repeated itself.

In one case Jean Hautefeuille, a young inventor from Orléans, France, substituted gunpowder for steam, thus anticipating the internal combusion engine by about three centuries. Just how precarious the operation of such an engine was, or even an experiment with one, can easily be imagined. For each stroke of the piston a fresh charge of gunpowder had to be somehow introduced and exploded.

The relative safety of steam convinced another inventor that steam was the true medium to employ in pushing the piston. Denis Papin, a Frenchman who eventually went to England and from there to Germany, developed the first use of steam to raise the piston and, upon its condensation, using atmospheric pressure, to drive the piston downward. One of the problems Papin faced, however, was the clumsiness of his engine. Water introduced into the cylinder below the piston was heated. It turned to steam and drove the piston upward. But then everyone had to wait while the fire was removed and the cylinder cooled off enough to let the steam condense to create a vacuum which permitted the atmospheric pressure on the opposite side of the piston to act and force it down.

The next step in the evolution of the steam engine was taken by Thomas Savery, an Englishman born about 1650. Logically it consisted of overcoming the clumsiness of Papin's engine, and the solution was to turn water to steam with the fire in a container separate from the rest of the engine and admitting the steam by means of a connecting pipe. This meant the fire did not have to be moved at all and each full cycle required less time. In fact, Savery's engine went through four complete cycles in one minute. He did not use the cylinder-piston arrangement of Papin but rather relied on the vacuum created by condensing steam to draw water upward to a reservoir where it was trapped by a valve. On the next cycle more water was drawn up, pushing the water on top farther up a pipe.

Savery's engine worked well enough with a trained assistant who could manipulate the valves regularly. He managed to move water up a distance of 62 feet, developing about one horsepower. But many of the flooded mines were over 250 feet deep and it was not practical to install a series of Savery's engines at various levels to get the water out. His invention was used to pump water to houses and that was all. But his contribution was the development of a boiler separated from the other parts of his engine.

The following advancement in the steam engine (alternately called a fire engine and an atmospheric engine) was of commercial importance and it was produced by Thomas Newcomen. It employed a separate boiler as Savery's had done but it returned to the idea of a vertically placed cylinder with a piston. The truly original innovation was the way in which steam within the cylinder was condensed. In Papin's earlier engine a jet of cold water played on the cylinder from the outside. Newcomen introduced the water directly into the cylinder, thus making condensation time less. Set up and working, the Newcomen engine in 1712 could make ten strokes a minute and raise ten gallons at one stroke. The water could be raised through 153 feet.

Newcomen produced these engines with slight modifications and they were in use when James Watt was born.

In 1759 James Watt was happily at work in his university instrument repair room. For a young man of that time his situation was enviable. He had work, an assured "situation" and the company of many excellent scientists. Until this time he had given no particular thought to steam engines, although he certainly was aware of their existence. At some time during 1759 his friend, Dr. John Robison, stopped by for a chat. As was customary the talk ranged over a number of subjects, and Robison brought up the subject of steam engines. They were mostly of the Newcomen type and primarily were used to raise water from wells or drain mines. Robison suggested—in a flight of fancy—that such an engine might well have a wider field of use. Suppose, he wondered aloud, they were connected to the woolen looms and could drive those, and also suppose they could be installed aboard ships and used to drive them, or placed in some kind of wagon and move the wagon along a road.

Both men saw the possibilities at once and it was this "daydreaming session" that, Watt wrote later, set him on the path toward perfecting the steam engine, turning it into the first widely used power plant since the dawn of civilization.

Unlike his precursors in the field of steam engine invention, Watt had the valuable combination of a scientific background, the heart of an engineer, and the skill of an instrument maker. During the next two years Watt studied the problem in every conceivable way. He built a small model engine using the positive force of steam to raise a piston. When the piston reached a reasonable height in the cylinder, he opened a valve and let the steam escape. The piston, of course, descended. He found he could raise as much as fifteen pounds with that first engine. The next phase of his work started by chance. In the university there was a working model of a Newcomen type engine—the type that relies on creating a vacuum beneath the piston and allowing atmospheric pressure to drive the piston down (hence atmospheric engine). The model, in any event, was supposed to work but for some reason it didn't. The university sent the engine to London for repair but on its return, Dr. Anderson, the professor involved, found it still would not work. In 1763 he took it to Watt and asked if he could "make the thing go." Watt fell to studying the Newcomen engine and analyzing every part of it. His engineering instinct, a horror of waste of any sort, came forth in this examination. He saw that the model—and probably the working full-scale engines— were losing the energy of steam at many points in the engine. In the first place, the boiler was not insulated and much of the heat of steam went through the boiler walls and was lost heating the surrounding air. He also saw that the flame used to heat the water in the boiler was not directing all of its energy to the boiler—much of that heat also raised the air temperature. The connecting tube to the cylinder was not insulated and so on and so on.

Watt calculated that probably three-fourths of the heat from the fuel never reached the cylinder to drive the piston upward. Most of this waste, he decided, took place in the cylinder itself —for the Newcomen engine, remember, relied on a jet of water introduced into the cylinder itself to condense the steam. This cooled the cylinder walls, which meant that much of the new steam coming in was used to reheat the metal walls of the cylinder.

At this stage Watt, perhaps without realizing it, was thinking of heat as a form of energy which was capable of doing work, i.e., moving the piston. With his instinct for efficiency he was trying to transfer as much of the fuel's heat energy as possible to the business of moving the piston. And while we have today much more complex and sophisticated methods of determining what we call the efficiency of engines, Watt was proceeding step by laborious step toward the same goal: elimination of waste. Another fault of Newcomen's engine came to Watt's attention. That was the jet of water itself that was squirted into the cylinder. It had to be removed, naturally, but more than that, it was not totally efficient, that is, it did not produce a very "high" vacuum. This meant that the atmosphere pressing on the opposite side of the piston was opposed by some remaining pressure within the cylinder, and of course this, too, was waste.

With true scientific instinct, Watt set about studying the properties of steam. Unwittingly he duplicated Professor Black's measurement of the heat (caloric) found in steam. As has already been mentioned, this energy amounts to approximately 540 calories per gram of steam. In Newcomen's engine very nearly all of this energy was thrown away—a fact which would produce nightmares for efficiency-minded engineers.

Watt himself could not explain this enormous energy in steam and he asked Professor Black about it. Black told him of his theory of latent or hidden heat. Had either of them known the energy necessary to "pull" water molecules apart to form the gaseous phase of water, he would have realized that it was not so mysterious. But the molecular theories of matter and the idea of conservation of energy being a natural fact had not been uncovered at that time.

When Watt had finished analyzing the Newcomen engine and the behavior of steam he was ready to work on his model. He did not want to cool the cylinder with each stroke of the piston—he wanted to keep the cylinder as hot as possible. The question of how he could condense the steam to produce the vacuum without cooling the cylinder was of outstanding importance. He knew also that he wanted to get rid of water in the cylinder and all possible amounts of air to produce as high a vacuum as possible.

In a real sense Watt's great experiment had been completed when he had finished his research and had the exact and critical problems laid out before him. The question of "how to accomplish the task" was to come in one of those often spoken about but rarely true "flashes of inspiration."

In his later papers Watt reported the moment of inspiration: ". . . I had gone to take a walk on a fine Sabbath afternoon. I had entered the Green by the gate at the foot of Charlotte Street—had passed to the old washing-house. I was thinking upon the engine at the time and had gone so far as the Herd's house when the idea came into my mind that, as steam is an elastic body (i.e. can be compressed and made to flow from high pressure to low pressure), it would rush into a vacuum, and if communication were made between the cylinder and an exhausted vessel, it would rush into it, and might there be condensed without cooling the cylinder. I then saw that I must get quit of the condensed steam and injection water, if I used a jet as in Newcomen's engine. Two ways of doing this occurred to me: first the water might be run off by a descending pipe . . . and any air might be extracted by a small pump; the second was to make the pump large enough to extract both water and air."

By his own admission, he could scarcely wait to see if the "inspiration" would hold up under experiment. The next day he began the construction of a model to test his idea. The historic engine model was saved and is preserved today in the Science Museum in London. Examination of it shows that it indeed was constructed in haste—so much haste in fact that one pipe was closed off by using a sewing thimble, taken, so legend has it, from his wife's sewing basket. To Watt's intense satisfaction, the model supported his idea and he set about next improving it and undertaking the building of a full-sized engine. His pump did draw off steam, air and water from his separate "condenser," as it was called, and the vacuum created drew the steam from the cylinder just as he had envisioned.

Through many years Watt worked to perfect his engine and its application. He knew that since the cylinder no longer was cooled it could be maintained at as high a temperature as the steam raised it—so he insulated the cylinder to prevent surrounding air from cooling it. He eventually devised a mechanical linkage connected with the piston rod which converted the reciprocal motion of the rod into rotary motion so the engine could drive wheels and thus power the looms of England. The idea of the linkage also permitted the eventual development of the steam locomotive and ushered in the era of rail transportation.

At the time of Watt's development of the steam engine the motion of the piston was transmitted to one end of a lever which acted as a rocker arm. The other end worked a pump piston for draining mines or merely raising water from a well.

Another important development perfected by Watt was a double-acting piston-cylinder arrangement. Instead of relying on atmospheric pressure to push the piston downward as in Newcomen's engine, Watt reasoned that since steam could exert more pressure than the atmosphere, he might as well introduce steam on the formerly open side of the piston, and drive the piston back with the energy of hot steam. By an arrangement of valves, this eventually was accomplished.

While, by today's standards Watt's first engine was not at all powerful, it was sufficiently powerful to be a commercial success.

His greatest troubles in developing the engine were (a) lack of money and (b) lack of precision machining for the parts of the engine, particularly the cylinder and piston arrangement.

The money aspect eventually was overcome by entering into a partnership with Matthew Boulton, a vigorous and enter-- prising businessman who saw the commercial possibilities of Watt's engine. The second problem was not solved so quickly. Machining metal in the eighteenth century was in a very primitive state and Watt knew that unless the inside shape of the cylinder, the piston and all valving were constructed ac- curately, great losses and excessive wear on the engine would result.

For the remainder of his life Watt worked to improve his engine. He developed a gauge that could measure the steam pressure in the cylinder while the engine was operating. Since this pressure changes from moment to moment as the piston proceeds along the cylinder, this gauge which recorded the changing pressure was a notable accomplishment in itself.

As the years passed and Watt's engine became more and more widely used, mankind was introduced to mechanical power on a large scale for the first time. The industrial age came on with a rush. Wool workers no longer carded, spun and wove wool at home. They were brought together in large factories and with belt-driven machinery increased their output many times.

As machines were developed to take advantage of steam power, production of goods in all parts of Europe rose and in exporting these goods in trade with the rest of the world, Eng- land's stature and wealth increased as did that of Germany and France. Among them these three nations dominated the civilized world in the latter part of the eighteenth century and all of the nineteenth century. As the factory system of production came to the young United States, it, too, increased its rate of development. But during all of the nineteenth century and the early years of the twentieth century, the United States was busy expanding to the shores of the Pacific Ocean. When that westward trek was complete, the United States began expending its productive energies in trade abroad and emerged as a world power of great consequence.

Today we have the internal combustion engine, jet engines, turbines and atomic engines which can produce awesome amounts of power. The spur to their development came as men saw through the application of steam power a widening horizon—and it was Watt who gave the world practical steam power to do a thousand tasks.

Honors came to James Watt in his last years from all parts of the world. He had been elected to the Royal Scientific Society years before but he refused an offer from the King to be made a member of the aristocracy—preferring seclusion and quiet in his last years. James Watt died in 1819. Probably his greatest honor came when the scientific unit of power was given his name, the watt. We see it most frequently today in the multiple of a thousand as we pay our electric bills in terms of the kilowatt-hour.

Thomas Edison: Man of Light

Of all varieties of genius, the kind Americans understand best is the practical type, the brilliance that solves immediate, tangible problems. They prefer a dramatic invention to an abstract theory. Albert Einstein, for example, was the butt of jokes made by many people who did not understand what he was doing and saw no workaday benefit in it; Thomas Edison, on the other hand, was revered by millions during his lifetime for his inventions. Edison was a practical man, a man who thought in terms of profit and loss and hard cash investment, a man who made things work. He was as American as apple pie. Or so the press of his day presented him to his eager public.

In reverent tones, *The New York Times* of June 24, 1923, reported:

"There is one human brain that has a hard cash market value today, in the business and industrial world, of $15,000,000,000. Billions is correct, not millions. That is within 20 per cent of equalling the value of all the gold dug from the mines of the earth since America was discovered.

"The brain is that of Thomas Alva Edison. . . ."

Extending its worshipful attitude farther, the *Times* listed the dollar value of investments in America in his inventions and cautioned its readers that the list contained "only the high spots."

Years before Thomas Alva Edison died in 1931, myth and

legend had begun to obscure the man and his work. During his life, millions of words were written about him, for he was always good "copy" for newspapers and periodicals. Many of the words contributed to the myths and legends, the overly dramatized or downright inaccurate stories purporting to be fact. And some of Edison's own words did too. Once, when telling how the concert violinst Eduard Reményi used to come by his office after hours and play for Edison and his associates "free," Edison jokingly said that Reményi occasionally played as much as "$2,000 worth."

It is certain that Edison knew the value of a dollar and respected the necessity of money; but he never confused ends with means and to him money was a means to an end. Edison always put money to work for him to further the great passion of his life: experimenting.

The list of his successful experiments is staggeringly large but among the best known are: Improved methods of telegraphy, quadruplex and multiplex, invention of the phonograph, development of a telephone transmitter that made Bell's invention commercially valuable, invention of the workable incandescent electric bulb, improved design of electric generators and circuit equipment, development of the mimeograph machine and typewriter, motion picture camera and the electric locomotive.

All of his inventions have made life easier or more productive for the world but none has had the far-reaching effect of the incandescent bulb. Edison introduced the world to the modern form of light.

Thomas Alva Edison was born February 11, 1847, in Milan, Ohio, a small village on the Huron River. His father, Samuel Edison, had migrated from Canada in 1842, selecting Milan because of the flourishing river trade that seemed to insure continual growth for the midwestern town. The Edison family was of Dutch lineage and had come to the New World prior to the Revolution. Thomas's line of the family remained on the Loyalist side during the struggle for independence and as a result took refuge in Nova Scotia when the Revolution proved successful. But Samuel, Thomas's father, became mixed up in Canadian affairs, joining an insurrection sponsored by William Lyon Mackenzie, and when that proved to be a failure, he migrated in some haste to Milan.

The 1840's were frontier days in Ohio, and although the wilderness and Indians had been partially tamed, civilized amenities such as regular schooling by experienced teachers still were lacking. As the railroads moved west, they took away the river trade by which Milan flourished, and by-passed the town. When that occurred, Samuel Edison moved his family to Port Huron where Thomas, at the age of seven, began school. His formal schooling was as brief as anyone ever had. He attended for three months and then his mother, herself a former schoolteacher, took him out of school and tutored him herself.

Like the great Faraday before him, Edison eventually became a self-educated man but he never mastered the intricacies of formal mathematics. He did, however, soak up knowledge at a prodigious rate. Under his mother's guidance he waded through volume after volume of such formidable works as *The Decline and Fall of the Roman Empire,* Hume's *History of England,* and only stubbed his toe when he tackled Newton's *Principia* (which even well-educated men of Newton's time could not understand). Much of this reading was accomplished before Edison was twelve years old, but he was by no means a bookworm.

He played vigorously with the children of his neighborhood

and one of his first experiments consisted of having a gullible friend swallow some stomach-settling medicine which was known to produce gas—on the theory that with enough medicine in him, the young friend should soar above the earth. The friend only got stomach pains, requiring a physician's attention, while Edison received the attention of his father—which resulted in pains elsewhere.

At that early age, Edison began to collect chemicals and built a laboratory in the cellar of his home. He soon had an array of 200 bottles (all labeled POISON) but he had very little money with which to buy materials. To get some, Edison badgered his parents until they agreed to let him take a job as newsboy on the train running from Port Huron to Detroit. The round trip was 126 miles and the twelve-year-old Edison left on a train at seven in the morning and came back on one that arrived home at nine-thirty at night.

Had Edison turned solely to business, rather than to invention, doubtless he would have been remembered as one of the tycoons of his age. For he had not been on the train more than a few months when he launched into business. In Port Huron he opened two stores—one selling magazines and newspapers, the other fresh garden produce in season. He hired two boys to manage the stores for him. He received permission to hire another newsboy for a different run to and from Detroit, and later invaded a daily train carrying immigrants to western farmlands. To these people, mostly poor Scandinavians, he sold bread, tobacco and candy.

In 1862, when he was only fifteen, Edison showed his flair for business by taking advantage of the desire for news of Union casualties from the Battle of Shiloh. Rumors placed them at 60,000. Noticing the crowds waiting for word in Detroit, he ordered not his usual stock of one hundred papers for the return trip to Port Huron but a thousand. He then legged it over to the telegraph office and persuaded the operator to wire ahead that a great battle was in progress. That done he boarded the train with his stock of a thousand papers. Crowds at each stop clamored for them and by the time he reached Port Huron, he had so few papers left he could safely charge twenty-five cents apiece for them. He sold out.

The purpose of all this enterprise was to buy chemicals and other equipment for Edison's beloved experiments. But he discovered that leaving home at seven in the morning and returning at nine-thirty at night did not give him much time in his cellar laboratory. To overcome this problem he persuaded the conductor of his train to let him build a laboratory in an unused part of the baggage car where he kept his papers. Thus he and his experimental equipment jiggled to and from Detroit each day. With his surplus energy he undertook studies in electricity. His interest in the subject came from the telegraph system which at that time was the only link between cities and towns of the nation. Telegraphy in fact was an extremely "romantic" business in those days. Telegraph operators enjoyed a status among small children that space pilots do today. Edison responded to the romance of the subject by building his own telegraph line between his home and that of a neighbor.

Casting about to find something to fill the remaining gaps in his day, Edison decided the newspaper business, also highly romantic and closely linked to telegraphy, was the thing, and he set up a press in the baggage car, bought type, and soon was producing the *Weekly Herald* for four hundred customers.

Edison's first serious setback came from the unstable situation of trying to run a chemistry laboratory aboard a rocking, jolting train. As might have been foreseen, a jar containing phosphorus fell while he was absent and set the baggage car afire. Jointly

Edison and the conductor managed to put the fire out, but the conductor was so angry and frightened he literally "boxed the ears" of the young experimentalist and tossed boy, chemicals and printing press off the train. The one lasting result of this was that Edison was partially deaf the rest of his life.

Throughout his early years on the train to and from Detroit, Edison was very close to telegraphy. Its lines paralleled the tracks, its operators greeted the incoming trains and, with his curiosity, it was only natural that Edison should learn code and eventually take a job as a telegraph operator. Shortly after the fiasco aboard the traveling laboratory (returned now to the cellar of his home) Edison got a job as an operator. By the time he was sixteen he was night operator at Stratford Junction in Ontario, Canada.

His passion for experimenting nearly got him fired from this post. Every hour, stations were required to "check in" by sending to the central office their station code. His was Sf. But with his reading—still carried on at a prodigious rate—and his experimental work during the day, Edison felt he should get some sleep at night. Since this was when he was supposed to be awake, another problem clearly was present. He solved it by rigging the telegraph key to a notched wheel which in turn rotated as the clock hands did. Thus his signal went out automatically while he slept. Unfortunately, it was noticed by the central office that even immediately following receipt of his signal, Edison could not be roused to take a message. The upshot of this first step toward automation brought a severe reprimand down on Edison's head.

Like most other telegraph operators, Edison moved almost casually from place to place and job to job in those years during and shortly after the end of the Civil War. In turn, he worked in Canada, Michigan, Indiana, Ohio, Tennessee, Kentucky and

Louisiana. His speed in transmitting via the stuttering telegraph key became greater and greater and he could receive the most rapid transmission of other operators without blinking. His skill led to a job in Boston but by then his true interests in science and invention began to dominate his thinking.

He bought a complete set of Faraday's works on electricity and magnetism and began to study it. To his delight he found that Faraday, himself no mathematician, explained his principles in clear terms, terms that Edison understood and was to remember all his life. When he was not in the telegraph office, Edison was at his boardinghouse home, reading, experimenting, or out buying supplies for further experiments.

Edison's first patent (number 90,646) was granted him for an electrical vote recorder. Unfortunately its efficiency ran counter to the wishes of legislators and he found no buyers for his first patented invention. This failure to find a market for his brainchild taught Edison a sound lesson: if you plan to earn a living by experimenting and inventing, be sure somebody will buy what you invent.

Gradually, as he worked in the telegraph office in Boston, the resolve came to strike out on his own as full-time inventor. He had invented a stock ticker, the unsellable vote recorder, a dial telegraph system, and his knowledge of electrical circuits and mechanical devices was good. His head swarmed with ideas and he finally made a complete break, leaving his telegraphy job and going to New York to look for a job that would take him closer to his goal.

Mechanical devices to facilitate the exchange of information between businesses, the stock exchange and stock brokerage offices were being tried in New York. Various kinds of stock tickers had been marketed and nearly all of these depended on electrical circuits. This was Edison's field and he entered it, setting himself up in business with another young man as the electrical engineering firm of Pope, Edison & Co. Within a short time the Gold and Stock Telegraph Co. bought the company and the services of Edison and his partner, Franklin L. Pope. The Gold and Stock Telegraph Co. in turn was purchased by Western Union and its president, Marshall Lefferts, asked Edison to improve the crude stock ticker then in use. Edison set to work and in improving the system produced several minor inventions which he patented. When he was through Lefferts called him to his office, thanked him and said that he wanted to purchase the patents which Edison held for the components of the revised system. As Edison recalled it years later, he would have been willing to settle for as little as $3,000 but his business experience prompted him to ask Lefferts what he would pay for them. Lefferts dumbfounded Edison by suggesting $40,000.

In a daze, Edison accepted a check and went to the bank. He'd never been paid by check before and he wasn't sure what to do. He cashed the check finally, stuffed the money in his pockets and went to his boardinghouse. The cash made him so nervous that the next day he rushed to the bank and deposited it all—after being informed by Lefferts that such a procedure was the best thing to do.

With the money from Lefferts, Edison was able to enter the "business" of inventing and be freed from financial worry. It gave Edison his true start. In rapid order he developed and patented the so-called "quadruplex" telegraph, a system that permitted the sending of four messages simultaneously over a single wire. Next he developed the carbon-button transmitter which made Alexander Graham Bell's telephonic invention commercially practical. He invented the phonograph, the mimeograph and improved the typewriter. By 1877 young

Edison had come a long way. But his next major invention was to be no single stroke of genius, no flash of deduction or of intuition. It was to require months and years of unceasing work. Edison decided to set himself the task of producing a practical incandescent electric light.

He had been mildly interested in the problem for some time but the thing that set him to the task was a proposal of a friend, Professor George F. Barker, of the University of Pennsylvania. Edison had accompanied the professor and several other scientists to view an eclipse of the sun in Wyoming. Following the eclipse Edison joined a hunting party in Colorado. During those days of relaxation, Professor Barker asked Edison if he thought he could "subdivide" an electric current for lighting. The term "subdivide" has no meaning unless the state of electric lighting at that time is known. Actually lighting by electricity was well known in Edison's day. In fact, Faraday's mentor, Sir Humphry Davy, had demonstrated electric lighting as far back as 1809. Using a battery of 2000 cells he obtained enough voltage to draw an arc between the tips of two carbon rods, and the world saw its first arc light. This demonstration would have remained merely a laboratory curiosity had not Faraday discovered the principle of the dynamo or generator, for it obviously is not practical to have to use 2000 cells each time you want to turn on a light. But with the invention of the generator, experimenters had at hand a source of voltage large enough to draw arcs between tips of carbon rods, and by the 1870's several successful attempts had been made to produce general lighting in this manner. Arc lighting, however, had several disadvantages. Among them was the fact that each light consumed a great deal of current and had to be supplied by a single large generator. Thus if you wanted ten lights you had to use ten generators—an admittedly expensive proposition. Another disadvantage of arc lights was the extreme brilliance of the source. The arc when drawn across the carbon rod tips could not be looked at directly for more than a moment. Its light was intense and cast harsh shadows. Furthermore, the carbon tips gradually burned away and constant adjustment of the gap between the tips meant someone— or something—had always to be in attendance.

The term "subdivide" as Professor Barker used it meant devising some way literally to subdivide the current used in a single arc lamp and produce a number of less intense lights in different places. Edison knew at the very outset of his search that arc lighting could never be used successfully in the average home. Not only was it too expensive but it also was impractical because of the brilliance of the light and the heat generated at the carbon tips.

Light in homes of that day came from burning gas or oil. In cities gas lamps were common, and many companies generated gas from coal and piped it to the stores and homes of densely populated areas. Whale oil, candles and later kerosene provided fuel for lamps in rural areas.

What Edison wanted to produce when he began was an electrical lighting system in which lights would have the gentle, soft light of a gas flame and at the same time be economically possible. For it would do no good whatever to solve the problem of subdividing the current if, in doing it, the cost was prohibitive. Another goal he had in mind was to arrange his lights so that if one were turned on or off it would not affect others in the system.

At the outset of his long search he formed the Edison Electric Light Company financed with $300,000 capital and began to organize the fight at his experimental headquarters in Menlo Park, N.J.

On the question of subdividing the current, he had to face the ridicule of many world-famous scientists. They claimed that it simply couldn't be done and that Edison was wasting his time. One proved to his own satisfaction that subdividing current ran counter to the established law of the conservation of energy. Another remarked on the multitude of problems anyone would face in making electric lighting practical and economical and concluded by saying: "Knowing something of the intricacy of the practical problems, I should certainly prefer seeing it in Mr. Edison's hands to having it in mine."

So, as it turned out, did Edison. He set about the task with his enormous energy. At his laboratory in Menlo Park he organized workmen into shifts and they worked quite literally around the clock. The shifts were not of the usual variety. Men worked until they felt they needed sleep and when they did they frequently slept on tables in the laboratory. Day and night were indistinguishable to them. They worked, slept a few hours, ate and worked on. This curious arrangement of working time stemmed from the habits of Edison himself. For most of his life he required very little sleep. And once he tackled a problem, he wanted to continue working on it until it was solved completely. He could take a short nap stretched out on a table, be sound asleep for two or three hours and rise to take up the work where he had left it. The men he found suited to his style of working stayed with him and shared the bizarre working arrangement.

The first problem Edison tackled was that of finding a material which could be heated by an electric current until it became white hot without breaking or melting. His first thoughts turned to the element carbon and he succeeded in passing a current through a carbonized piece of paper and bringing it to incandescence. Of course oxygen from the atmosphere quickly burned up the filament and he knew that he had to produce his electric light in as high a vacuum as possible. Earlier researchers in the same direction had tried placing filaments in evacuated tubes but had met with only modest success. Some even had filled the bulbs with nitrogen gas which is very nearly inert chemically. This gas was used to exclude oxygen and reduce the chance of the filament's burning.

It became clear to Edison very early in the search that his principal problem was to find a material suitable for a filament. Its requirements were simply that it had to become incandescent before melting and had to have a very small cross-section area. The reason for the small cross-section area is clear when the economic part of the lighting problem is understood.

At the outset of organizing his assault on the problem, Edison studied the gas lighting industry in every detail. He made careful entries in his many notebooks regarding the cost of gas to consumers in various sections of New York City. To get these data he sent men around various neighborhoods where they actually counted the number of gas jets turned on in each house at hourly intervals, and when he was through studying the gas systems of his day he knew as much if not more than most gas company officials about the subject.

In Edison there was an infinite fund of patience which sustained him during all his laborious work. It, like his energy, apparently was inexhaustible. He never "hurried" but plodded methodically on and on for six weeks, six months or six years until a task was completed. One example of that patience was shown when, on a rare fishing trip with his employees off the New Jersey shore on a chartered boat, he sat with a baited hook over the side of the vessel for two days and two nights waiting for a bite. He never got one and was dissuaded from staying only by the pleas of his employees.

In his preliminary studies concerning gas lighting and what electrical lighting would have to offer to compete successfully, Edison knew that the filament of any incandescent light had necessarily to be of small cross-section area. He reasoned thus: I want the electrical heating to take place in the filament primarily with minimal heating of the conducting wires carrying current to the filament. The higher the resistance a wire has to the flow of current, the more heat is generated. And since the resistance of a wire is inversely related to its cross-sectional area, I want the filaments to be highly resistant, i. e. very small in cross-section area. The sense of this reasoning is obvious. If a customer pays for electricity which expends its energy in getting to the bulb rather than in bringing the bulb to incandescence, he will have to pay an exorbitant rate for electric lighting—and he'll continue to use gas.

Edison's initial tests with carbon filaments were only moderately successful. He managed to get carbon filaments to incandescence in a vacuum but they lasted only about fifteen minutes before they burned out. In these early stages of experimenting, he tried every form of paper, cardboard, and wood for filaments. The preparation of the filaments in each case was nearly the same. A thin strip of tissue paper, for example, would be rolled into thread and placed in an oven at high temperature. The paper, being composed of carbon, hydrogen and oxygen, turned black or carbonized as the gases of oxygen and hydrogen were driven off by the heat. The filament was allowed to cool and it was then carefully inserted in a glass bulb which was sealed off from the atmosphere and evacuated. The ends of the filament had been previously fixed to electrical connections running to the outside of the glass bulb and when a high vacuum was reached, current was passed through the filament. As its temperature rose, it turned first a dull red, then orange, and finally white as it reached full incandescence.

Such carbonized material as tissue paper is extremely brittle and very delicate. The slightest jar will break it. In an attempt to overcome its fragility, Edison used "hard" carbon from wood. He tried coating the filaments with lampblack, and soaking them in tar. To keep them from burning out or oxidizing, he tried sprinkling the filaments with powdered glass, hoping the glass would melt and coat the filament, thus protecting it from stray molecules of oxygen left in the bulbs. None of his attempts proved practical. He could get a filament to incandescence all right but it burned out or broke within minutes.

When he had tried every form of carbon he could think of, Edison turned to the idea of a metal filament. He experimented with platinum and found that he could make a filament of this expensive metal but that the temperature necessary to bring it to incandescence was only a little below the temperature at which it would melt. Thus if a slightly stronger current than necessary were used, the platinum melted. This was a serious drawback, since the regulation of voltages was poor in those days and any increase in the speed of the dynamo could send a surge of current through the lines—which then would melt all such platinum filaments.

And platinum, too, burned out anyway very shortly after current was sent through it. But it was during these experiments with platinum that Edison found the key to the problem of the burned-out filaments. With his expensive mercury vacuum pump he could produce very high vacuums—as high as one-millionth the pressure of the atmosphere. This was done, of course, to remove oxygen molecules from the bulb and thus prevent the oxidation or burning of the filament when it was heated by the electric current. It occurred to Edison while working with the platinum that the metal probably contained some oxygen molecules either sticking to the surface or mixed inside the metal itself during its refinement from the ore. He decided to heat the filament of platinum during the process of evacuating the bulb. The heat would drive the oxygen from the metal and the pump would extract this residual gas along with the oxygen of the atmosphere in the bulb.

Edison's tests with platinum and other metals did not prove successful, and he returned to his study of carbon, which he instinctively felt was the proper material. Carbon, he knew, had a great affinity for oxygen and if allowed to remain in the atmosphere within minutes would become coated with oxygen molecules. So he planned to produce a carbon filament and heat it while evacuating the bulb, as he had done with the platinum. The question of what form of carbon to use for the filament remained. He wanted it, as always, to be of very small cross section, and yet be durable. By this time he had tried nearly three thousand different kinds of filaments, and casting about for yet another material that by its structure would prove suitable, he decided to carbonize a piece of sewing thread.

Even today the practical problem of heating such a thread to carbonize it, allowing it to cool and then removing it and fastening it to the metal connections of the bulb is formidable. When Edison tried it, there were neither machinery nor tools designed to do that delicate work. It had to be done by hand.

Working with Charles Batchelor, one of his assistants, Edison set to the task. He bent the piece of thread into a horseshoe shape and placed it in the mold to be heated. When it was carbonized he carefully withdrew the filament and, followed by Batchelor, started to carry it to the glassblower's workshop to seal it in the bulb. It broke before they got there. With his monumental patience, Edison turned around and began again. He and Batchelor worked through one night, all the next day and through a second night. They used up an entire spool of thread. Once they got as far as the glassblower's shop and just as they were about to place the filament on the bench, it broke. Late on the afternoon of the second day they produced another filament—which was broken by a screwdriver. Before nightfall they had produced yet another filament and this they successfully placed in the bulb. Edison heated the filament as the vacuum pump was turned on and they waited until the gauge showed the pump had reached its limit. They had a vacuum equal to a millionth of an atmosphere. Then Edison turned the current on for full incandescence. The filament turned red, then orange, then white hot within the small glass bulb.

Although they had had little or no sleep for over forty-eight hours, neither Edison nor Batchelor felt tired. Their eyes were on the gently glowing bulb. They had reached incandescence before, so the sight was nothing new but each asked himself how long will it last? Other workmen gathered around the bulb and stared at it. Minutes ticked away and became hours. The men, half-seriously, half-jokingly, began to make bets on how long the bulb would burn.

Still more men came into the shop and stared, hypnotized, at the light. Shifts came and went. The word spread throughout the laboratory. For forty hours the bulb remained incandescent. When at last it burned out, Edison knew that he had a workable filament for the electric lamp. One of the goals Edison had set himself was to develop a lamp that would burn for one thousand hours before needing replacement. This was dictated by the economic necessity of competing with gas. And while forty hours was nowhere near a thousand, he knew he was on the right track. The date of producing that first workable incandescent lamp was October 21, 1879. It had taken thirteen months of continuous work by Edison's entire group of researchers and craftsmen, plus an expenditure of more than $40,000 for materials and costs above the usual laboratory operation.

Knowing now that he had to heat the filament while evacuating the bulb, Edison set to work manufacturing carbon filaments made from rolled paper. These worked as well as the thread filament and were easier to produce. It was not long before Menlo Park had electric lights in the laboratory, the various shops and the homes of Edison and his lieutenants.

Each worker in the project knew that while progress had been made, much more work was necessary before Edison would consider the project finished. But just how much work lay ahead, not even the wisest suspected. For although Edison had found a satisfactory form of carbon for a filament, he wanted a better form. He began by carbonizing as many different kinds of vegetable growth as he could put his hands on. Among the samples tried (and there literally were thousands) were coconut hair, flax, cedar shavings, cotton and hairs plucked from the beard of one of his colleagues. He searched far and wide for various grasses and reeds and cane. And then, as his biographers have recorded it, he was sitting thinking about filament materials one day when he picked up a palm-leaf fan. He saw that the edge of the fan was trimmed with a thin, long flexible strip of bamboo. When he had ripped that strip from the fan, carbonized it and tried it as a filament, he knew he had a much better material than thread or paper. At once he set about collecting different kinds of bamboo from all over the world.

There followed, for a period of nearly ten years, one of the most bizarre searches ever conducted on earth. Men were dispatched to South America, Asia and Japan to locate the "perfect bamboo." Packages arrived at Menlo Park from far up the

Amazon containing samples of different species. Each was tested thoroughly and the results were entered into Edison's voluminous notebooks. William H. Moore, an associate of Edison, went to China and Japan. One Japanese bamboo which showed up remarkably well in competition with all the other filament material was considered to be best, and Edison contracted with a Japanese producer of the bamboo to take all he could grow.

For years, all Edison's incandescent lamp filaments were made of this special bamboo until eventually tungsten supplanted the plant fiber.

As the work went forward from that day in October, 1879, news of Edison's success leaked out. And since Menlo Park was being lighted by his lamps, the more skeptical people who heard of the invention had only to walk through the little settlement after dark. Edison and his men were still so busy perfecting the lamp and working on the next phase of his project that they did not pause, at first, to publicize the discovery.

In Europe, scientists were still giving speeches explaining why Edison could not possibly "subdivide current" after he already had accomplished it. A New York reporter sent a story to his paper telling what Edison had done and this drew many businessmen, sightseers and scientists to Menlo Park. In fact, from the date of his discovery, Menlo Park became world famous and Edison himself was given his nickname "The Wizard of Menlo Park."

So intense was the excitement caused by the news that on New Year's Eve of 1879 a special train ran from New York to Menlo Park carrying 3000 people who wanted to see the new and entirely practical electric light. The lamps were strung on wires from tree to tree around the laboratory grounds and the awestruck crowds milled about staring at the small bulb, the delicate but efficient filament, and their faces were lighted by the twinkling of hundreds of the lamps.

It is impossible today to comprehend the excitement caused by an electric light bulb in 1879. Yet any glance at history shows that men always have exerted themselves to discover and use a more efficient form of light so they would not be dependent upon the sun. In early American days, tallow candles were used but these were so expensive for the average home that rush lights were more common. These consisted of nothing more than lake or stream rushes dried and soaked in grease. When held by a clamp on a stand and lit, they gave a wavering smoky light. Candles were reserved for special occasions such as the visit of a minister or some other person of note. Oil burning lamps have been known since Egyptian and Babylonian times. But in all cases, the light was smoky, wavering and not at all suited for reading or other fine work. With the invention of gas lighting early in the nineteenth century, men took a great step toward eliminating dependence on the sun. But even gas lighting had its serious drawbacks. Its fumes could foul a closed room quickly; it needed a supply of oxygen to burn; it caused fires; and it hissed as the gas burned. In addition, breaks in the gas lines in a city frequently were the cause of explosions and conflagrations.

When Edison set out to "beat the gas companies" with electric lighting, he knew that he had much more to do than invent an incandescent bulb that copied the soft, steady glow of gaslight. He had to devise an entire system for distributing electricity in correct amounts and at prices that would compete with those of the gas companies.

With these thoughts in mind, Edison devised the lamp so that the filament had a high resistance, and he planned to use relatively large copper wires to supply current to the lamps.

These supply lines had to be of low resistance, which meant the larger they were in cross-section area, the better. But copper costs money too, so there was a practical or economic limit to the size of copper wire he could use.

The circuit he used for his lamps was such that if one lamp burned out it did not affect the other bulbs burning on the same line. He used the presently well-known parallel arrangement of lamps where the two copper feeders ran parallel and the lamps were connected at intervals between the feeders. Each lamp drew the correct current according to the laws of "multiple circuits," as parallel systems were termed in those days. With high resistance filaments, he generated heat or "used" the electrical energy where he wanted to—in the lamps—while the low resistant feeders passed the current along without developing much heat. This was his method of doing the impossible, of subdividing the current.

Edison knew that despite his success in developing a practical incandescent lamp, he had to do three more important things before the electric lamp could begin to replace gas for lighting: (1) develop a power station that could generate the necessary current; (2) provide unceasing service to customers and (3) lay out the main and feeder lines, as he called them, and install circuits in individual buildings.

His first problem, of developing an efficient generating station, again brought him into conflict with scientists of his time. Although the principle of the dynamo or generator was known through Faraday's researches, no detailed analysis of the generators had been made. But Edison knew that the best generator of his time wasted a lot of energy in the generator itself. Since he had to meet economic competition, he had to get rid of as much waste as he could. In 1879, while still working on the bulb, Edison set some of his men to work to redesign an electric

generator to make it more efficient. After months of work and
exhaustive examination of every part of the generator, F. R.
Upton, with the help of the craftsman John Kruesi, built a generator that proved to be 90 per cent efficient. That is, it converted 90 per cent of the mechanical energy put into rotating
it into usable electrical energy. This in itself was a major
accomplishment, made all the more astonishing by the fact
that no one in the world had analyzed all the electrical, magnetic and mechanical aspects of generators before and overcome
the difficulties so successfully. The best generators produced
before Edison's redesigning had proved less than 50 per cent
efficient.

When Upton announced publicly that they had a 90 per cent
efficient generator, Menlo Park, Edison and Upton were deluged
with complaints that such a claim was obvious nonsense.
Manufacturers wrote in and visited, demanding to see proof of
the claim and to be instructed in the process of designing such
machines. Mr. Upton had the additional problem of informing
all who came to scoff how the Edison generators were constructed.

Still not content with his generators, Edison had a large high-
speed generator designed that would do the work of ten of the
smaller low-speed generators. He understood very well the
principles of Faraday, one of which relates the size of the
voltage generated to the speed of the wires rotating within a
magnetic field. An increase in speed means an increase in
voltage.

Edison set his sights on a small section of New York City
as the place for his first venture into what we call today, as
he did then, the "central station electric lighting plant." He
bought two buildings and cleared the interiors and there he
set up his huge, high-speed generators. Miles of wires carefully

insulated were buried in conduits along the streets leading into the buildings to be served. Millions of dollars were being gambled in the last phase of Edison's dream of lighting by electricity.

At the outset of his project in 1877, Edison had formed the Edison Electric Light Company, and he carried much of the risk himself as the work went forward. Men with money to invest looked, as always, with suspicion on a new idea, a new concept. The public itself was astonished by the electric lamp, but it knew nothing of the problems or intricacies of designing and building generators or of supplying current to various buildings. So while the plant was being built and the lines laid, Edison and some of his men had to try to "sell" the idea to people. From an office in New York City near the site of the Pearl Street power station, Edison put lighting and himself on display.

It did not, however, take him from his work. He literally watched every installation, every wire being laid in the entire system. He overcame difficulties in the high-speed generators and the direct coupling shafts connecting them to the steam engines which drove them. On September 4, 1882, the generators were started, the switches thrown and at three o'clock in the afternoon of that day, four hundred lamps went on. But not until sunset was the effect very dramatic. As daylight faded, workers in the stores on Fulton Street from Nassau to the East River went on about their tasks almost unaware that the sun had gone down. The soft, gentle glow of electric lamps gave them plenty of light by which to finish their work. Passersby stopped on the street and stared at the lighted windows. In them there was none of the flicker of gaslight—and only about six per cent of the heat released by burning gas.

The generators in the Pearl Street power station ran with

but one slight interruption for thirteen years. As more lines were laid, more generators were added. By 1889 even the most cautious investor realized that there was money to be made in the growing electric light industry, and the Edison General Electric Company was formed with a capital of $12,000,000. It exists today in New York, along with hundreds of other modern power companies, and is a multibillion dollar business.

And what of Edison? With all his instinct for commerce, he never made a dollar from his invention of the incandescent bulb. When the Edison General Electric Company was formed, he sold out. His profits he put into other, more pressing work, more experiments. His uncontested right to the invention of the incandescent bulb was delayed for years and there were over two hundred lawsuits costing nearly $2,000,000 fighting infringement cases. For when the light was first described in news reports, many people in the United States and abroad saw "how simple it all was" and began producing their own—claiming originality. The patent for such an invention ran for seventeen years—after which time it no longer could be protected. Edison fought infringement cases for fourteen of those seventeen years. Three years after he finally established his claim in court, the incandescent bulb became public property.

Edison turned back to his laboratory, to his experiments. There were several ideas that intrigued him. There was the idea of an electrically operated locomotive . . . an ore processing idea . . . a scheme he had for producing Portland cement more efficiently . . . and then there was the one for taking many pictures of people rapidly and projecting them on a screen. That intrigued Edison, so he went to work. Imagine, seeing pictures of people walking around on a large white screen. Incredible!

The Wright Brothers: Men with Wings

Say the word "aviator" and a jauntily capped, dashing figure quite likely springs to your mind. Say "inventor" and a cavernous laboratory with a bespectacled, bushy-headed worker is conjured up; "scientist" and a high-foreheaded intellectual may emerge. But say "inventors of the airplane" and what appears is a picture of two men wearing derby hats, high starched collars, and nondescript gray suits, looking as undistinguished as a Monday morning.

Wilbur and Orville Wright were as colorless as a gray day in December. Photographs of them are rare and if, in their time, they had stepped away from their astonishing invention and stood within the watching crowd, they would have been impossible to locate a moment later. They had no glamour. They said nothing outstanding at interviews. They rarely smiled. They shunned publicity and the press, and they refused all offers to "get their story across" to the people of the world. They had little formal education and so were not trained scientists in the scholastic sense. Yet these two men, bicycle manufacturers from Dayton, Ohio, gave wings to the world and realized man's centuries-old dream of flying.

Even today, argument surrounds their accomplishment, for they were not the first men of their generation or earlier ones to try to build a heavier-than-air flying machine—one that could move forward, rise from level ground, go in any desired direction and land safely. Despite all the argument since their time, the world has finally acknowledged that Wilbur and Orville Wright did indeed develop and fly the first practical airplane and, as Wilbur would have been first to say, did it without borrowing money from anybody.

On Kill Devil Hill at Kitty Hawk, North Carolina, on the 17th of December, 1903, the Wrights' airplane moved forward under its own power, rose from the ground and flew, coming down at the same level as take-off and without injury to the pilot or damage to the plane. It is true that the flight was of short duration, only twelve seconds, but immediately following it, three more flights were made and Wilbur Wright stayed aloft in their gasoline-engine powered glider for fifty-nine seconds and the plane traveled 852 feet.

The story of that dramatic flight on the windswept dunes along the North Carolina coast does not begin there. It begins in the small bicycle shop in Dayton, Ohio. For, in a peculiar way, being bicycle manufacturers was a great help to Wilbur and Orville Wright when they first studied the problem of manned, powered flight.

From time immemorial man has dreamed of flying. Historians link this urge to primitive man's concept of the sky's being the dwelling place of gods and the natural desire to mingle with them. Psychologists somewhat less romantically might explain the desire to fly by stating that it is merely a desire to escape earthly troubles and disappointments. Whatever the reason, man has always envied the birds of the air, and in one of the first recorded efforts at flight the mythological Greek experimenter, Icarus, and his father Daedalus, in trying to escape from prison, fashioned huge bird wings of many feathers, holding them together with wax, and flew. Unfortunately, Icarus, according to the legend, flew too near the sun, whose heat melted the wax and sent him plunging into the sea, while his father flew on and escaped.

Late in the fifteenth century, Leonardo da Vinci made sketches of a flying machine that bore a remarkable resemblance to the skeletal structure of birds. Da Vinci's machine was never built, although much later, in Europe, many experimenters were led astray by trying to copy the motion of bird wings to sustain a man in flight. Such machines, called ornithopters, have been tried many times but never successfully. In the sixteen hundreds and as late as 1780, experimenters worked to produce some form of glider—for men had noticed that many birds were able to stay aloft without moving their wings as they rode air currents up and down at their pleasure. But all attempts to produce a man-carrying glider failed then, too. In 1783 in France a chance discovery turned men's attention away from winged aircraft. It was found that heated air, enclosed in a light container, could raise the container through the cooler surrounding air, and so the age of man-carrying balloons captured everyone's attention. In November of that year hydrogen gas was discovered and found to be much lighter than even heated air. The fact that it was flammable, of course, made it dangerous, but not so dangerous that it kept men on the ground. Balloons soared over Paris and the surrounding countryside. Clubs of balloonists were formed in Europe and later in the United States. The military services of all nations saw in balloons a means of observing the enemy from the air and made use of them in that way.

The balloon age of flight lasted a little more than a century and was ended by the disastrous attempt of a Swedish scientist and balloonist, Salomon Andrée, to drift over the North Pole in the largest balloon built up to that time. The balloon had a volume of 176,500 cubic feet which was filled with hydrogen.

After careful preparation, on July 11, 1897, Andrée and two companions left from Dane's Island in the Spitsbergen group. They carried thirty-two carrier pigeons which they planned to release with messages from time to time. It was the last the world saw of these aerial pioneers. For thirty-three years their fate was unknown and then, in 1930, an expedition found the bodies of the men on White Island about one hundred miles from their starting place. The recovered diaries revealed that the balloon had gone three hundred miles north and crashed. The men had crossed ice floes covering two hundred miles to land before they perished.

All interest in heavier-than-air flying machines had not been wiped out by the balloon craze, however. Sir George Cayley in the middle of the nineteenth century developed a remarkably prophetic glider. It had many of the features that were to be present on the planes built by such experimenters as S. P. Langley and Wilbur and Orville Wright. The list of these earliest pioneers like Cayley is very long. Among the outstanding men on it are Felix du Temple, Otto Lilienthal, Alphonse Penaud, F. H. Wenham, Victor Tatin, and Clement Ader. All of these men contributed their efforts to find a way to put men in the air safely in a guidable aircraft. Most important of these early pioneers for the Wright Brothers was Otto Lilienthal, a German, who developed the first workable glider that would carry a man. The guiding principle that Lilienthal used was the pilot himself. By moving his body back and forth and from side to side, the pilot was supposed to balance and direct the flight of the machine. But Lilienthal himself was killed while testing his glider—though not before he made many successful flights.

In America another scientist, Octave Chanute, was to prove himself of great value to the Wright Brothers. In many ways

Chanute was the patriarch of aeronautical science. He gave help freely to all experimenters and hopeful inventors. His knowledge of what science knew about flying was encyclopedic and he himself built various kinds of gliders to test his own theories of flight. That neither he nor any of the others successfully solved the problem was not due to lack of effort. One reason for their failure may well have been that they knew—and cared—nothing about bicycles.

Wilbur Wright was the older of the two brothers. He was born in 1867 and Orville in 1871. Two other older brothers and a younger sister completed the totally undistinguished family. The father, Milton Wright, edited a religious publication and later became a bishop in a small Protestant sect. Their mother, Susan Wright, was college-educated and was a good, typical midwestern wife. Both of the Wrights' older brothers as well as their younger sister attended college but neither Wilbur nor Orville went beyond high school in formal education. Wilbur, as a matter of fact, dropped out of school when he was about thirteen and went to work. Orville completed high school and then joined his brother in business.

Their life as boys and as young men reveals nothing whatever of the quality termed "genius." Both were shy and reserved. Wilbur was the less responsive of the pair; in later years Orville was seen to smile on several occasions. Wilbur rarely smiled at all and never in public.

When men achieve some outstanding goal, biographers usually begin the search among the files of background sources: friends, letters, remembered incidents by the persons themselves in order to reconstruct, if not create, a colorful personality and sufficient reasons to explain the astonishing success. The Wrights have very nearly defied the most microscopic examination. If, at the time of their young manhood, some prophetic biographer had encountered them and examined every detail of their lives, he would have left without a story. They were honest, abstemious, hard-working and they had the usual middle-class respect for a dollar. But many young men in Dayton, Ohio, in 1892 shared those qualities. Millions of Americans lived exactly as the Wrights did.

In the intensive search to account for the Wright Brothers' achievement, a few clues have turned up. As bishop of the small religious sect, Milton Wright frequently had to chastise various ministers. Some of them, outraged, wrote or placed stories in newspapers which did not ruffle Milton Wright's equanimity in the least. He simply ignored the newspapers. Wilbur and Orville in later years applied that method and ignored attacks, entreaties and condemnations concerning them which appeared in newspapers.

Something also has been made of the fact that the Wright Brothers always worked for themselves—they never "hired out." In this fact one writer finds an uncommon development of independence and of ability to achieve goals which were self-created. This may be true—but then it ought to be true equally of every small businessman who is self-employed throughout the country—and it isn't.

There is, unquestionably, some value in remembering that Wilbur and Orville Wright worked together in close harness all their lives. At an early age they found that their interests were remarkably similar and they opened a joint venture in 1892: a bicycle repair shop. Both liked machinery; both derived great satisfaction in solving mechanical problems. And conceivably both enjoyed the quiet and solitude of labor in the shop, away from the disconcerting rest of humanity. Each stimulated the thinking of the other and in each other's company escaped the depression of loneliness which frequently overtakes the solitary worker.

There is evidence of a great fund of curiosity in both the Wright Brothers but it was directed toward intensely practical ends. As youngsters they designed and flew kites—and experimented with different shapes and sizes to discover the most efficient. They discussed the crude, early automobiles that were being talked of and occasionally seen. They also tended to business, the business of bicycles and, a few years after opening the shop, they were manufacturing their own machines and continuing the repair business. Both brothers read widely in the exciting fields of science and unquestionably this reading was what set them on the trail toward human flight.

There was little in Wilbur's make-up to suggest a romantic nature but he became enamored of the idea of flying through learning of Otto Lilienthal's glider experiments in Germany. It set the practical young man to daydreaming. He and Orville followed Lilienthal's efforts with growing interest and both were upset when Lilienthal was killed. They began searching the library for more material on the then purely theoretical science of aeronautics. Not finding what they looked for, they decided to write to the Smithsonian Institution to send them material published by earlier pioneers, including the recently deceased Lilienthal. They were sent Professor Langley's *Experiments in Aerodynamics* as well as Octave Chanute's *Progress in Flying Machines*. Both brothers drew the same conclusion after reading the material they had received: very little actual progress had been made by experimenting. There were a great number of theories and many of the scientists concerned about the problem had built models to test. Lilienthal remained the favorite pioneer of the Wrights for he had actually built and flown gliders which could carry a man. But they also realized that the flights he made, while numerous, were spaced over weeks or months and that, in short, Lilienthal did not have a continuing body of experience to guide him. What he had learned about controlling his glider on one occasion, he had to relearn several weeks later on his next attempt. This seemed to be a great waste of experience to the Wrights.

In this belief they were making instinctive use of their own experience with bicycles. They knew that if a person wanted to learn to ride a bicycle he had to do more than coast a few feet for ten seconds every month or so. He had to give his body and nervous system continuing conditioning so that the muscles responded automatically to changes in the bicycle's position and speed. They knew that only through such efforts could the cycling machine be mastered. They saw no reason why this same conditioning should not also apply to a flying machine.

Many scientists and engineers who studied the problem of flight completely overlooked this valuable approach. Some, like S. P. Langley, built models and observed them. Others, like Octave Chanute, built full-scale gliders but also spent many hours observing their actions when they were flown as kites and they did not submit to the actual experience of flight. It was not the difference of courage—for there unquestionably was great danger in actual testing. Rather it was the difference in background of the experimenters. Scientists observed and recorded the results of the observations. A bicyclist tries and falls off and tries again and eventually learns to control the machine.

The Wrights held another advantage over their predecessors and contemporaries. Many of them were searching for a means of automatic control of their gliders. They believed—and Chanute held this belief—that proper design of a glider would give it a natural stability of its own, a stability that would level the wings when they were tipped by a gust of wind, or raise the front of the glider when it turned downward. To the Wrights this seemed as futile as attempting to develop an automatic bicycle. They knew from their own experience that the cyclist must control the machine at all times and in all ways. The machine, in short, had to become an extension of the rider. Likewise a glider had to become an extension of the pilot, responsive to the pilot's wishes and so constructed with guiding mechanisms as to allow the pilot to adjust the machine to changing conditions. Birds, they fully understood, controlled their wings and tails in flight, they altered their position in the wind and so were successful.

Much of this seems obvious to us today but in the late nineteenth century it was anything but obvious.

Many different schemes were tried on early gliders to give them an inherent stability: the center of gravity was placed well below the wings of the glider so its weight would tend to keep it level—or bring it to a level position if it tipped. This resulted in an oscillation or swinging motion and did not stop the tipping at all. Another design gave the wing a large dihedral, or slope upward from the center similar to that of many birds, in the hope of gaining stability. This, too, proved unsuccessful.

While pondering the problem one day in the bicycle shop Orville came up with the idea that the wingtips might be twisted by controls to change the angle between them and the flowing air. For it was known that if a wing was turned upward so the wind struck its underside, the wing moved up. Why not, Orville reasoned, design a wing so the force of the wind itself could level the glider?

By the time this idea occurred to the Wright Brothers, they had read most of the literature available on aeronautics. It struck them as odd that no one had thought of this obvious solution

before—and tried it. As a matter of fact it had been thought of
before but never tried. From that moment on, the Wrights were
on the correct course but they had to overcome the intensely
practical problem of how to twist the wingtips. Orville designed
a mechanism to turn them but it added too much weight to the
frame. Then, according to the Wrights' later story of the
development of their idea, Wilbur was serving a customer in
the bicycle shop when he found the solution. The customer had
purchased an inner tube for a bicycle tire and Wilbur was talking to him, toying with the cardboard box that had held the
inner tube. He twisted the box slightly, bending the broad surface of one side. He glanced down and saw that one end was
twisted upward, the other downward. Instantly he realized that
the wing of a glider could easily be "warped" that way and
the effect would be to change the angles of the wingtips with
regard to the wind. It would take no heavy, complicated
machinery to do the trick. The Wrights never wavered from
this concept and when they were successful, their method of
wing warping formed one of the chief arguments for their
patent.

By the time they had reached this fundamental conclusion,
the Wrights were momentarily stopped. They knew all the
theory of gliders and they had some ideas of their own. The
next step was to try them out. In approaching this part of the
problem, in May of 1900 they wrote their first letter to Octave
Chanute, who then was living in Chicago. Wilbur wrote and
explained what they proposed to try and the reasons for their
belief in the idea of wing warping. They also asked Chanute
where they might find an area for experimenting where winds
were steady and common. Chanute replied generously, en-
couraging them to continue, and suggesting they might find
the coastal area around San Diego, California, or St. James

City, Florida, to their liking. But one of the conditions of weather and geography the Wrights wanted was an abundance of sand dunes or sand hills from which they could glide and return to earth on comparatively soft, yielding terra firma. Chanute then suggested the coastal area of North Carolina. Accordingly the Wrights posted a letter to the Weather Bureau station at Kitty Hawk, North Carolina, and received a favorable reply. Wind was plentiful and fifteen miles per hour was the average. There was also a superabundance of sand, miles of it, in fact.

The almost stolid thoroughness with which the Wrights developed the plans for testing a glider is characteristic of them. Methodical, logical and attentive to every detail, they decided that in the fall of 1900 when the summer bicycle rush had slackened, they would go to Kitty Hawk with a glider and try out their ideas. In designing their first large glider, they chose a "double-decker" arrangement of wings which had been developed by Chanute. An engineer by training, Chanute had worked with bridge trusses and he knew the principles of such structures gave great strength. So the "biplane," as it later was termed, was an adaptation of the Chanute "double decker."

Late in the summer of 1900, Wilbur and Orville began the construction of their first glider. Actually their methodical approach masked a growing passion to fly and to be the first to fly—to win the prize of immortality. They found, as they used all their spare time working on the problem, that their enthusiasm began to take their minds from their business. Being cautious and hard-headed businessmen, they knew this could prove disastrous but, for the time being, there was nothing they could do about it. During August of that year they constructed the glider, sewing cloth for the wings, shaping the wooden frame and providing metal fasteners to hold the parts together.

The parts consisted of the two wings and their supporting members, a small "elevator" mounted horizontally forward of the wings. In this first machine they introduced the wing-warping idea, using wires from the pilot's platform to do that job.

They agreed that Wilbur would journey with the glider parts to Kitty Hawk in advance of Orville, who would "tend to business" in the bicycle shop as long as possible. Accordingly Wilbur took the train to Elizabeth City, North Carolina, with most of the glider packed and stowed in the baggage car. From Elizabeth City he managed to get passage on a small ship which took him to the long sand bar offshore. It stretches for many miles along the coast, but was not at that time connected to the mainland by a bridge.

The Wrights had brought with them all the parts for the glider except the wing spars, large pieces of wood which both felt could be found at or near Kitty Hawk and shaped to fit. They had planned on eighteen-foot spars but the longest timbers Wilbur could find were sixteen feet and he had to be content with them. After spending a few nights in the home of one of the citizens of Kitty Hawk, he pitched a tent on the sand dunes in a favorable spot, dragged the packaged glider parts to it and summoned Orville.

Orville arrived late in September and the two brothers quickly assembled their first glider.

To test the glider at first, the Wrights, with several helpful onlookers from the weather station, flew it as a kite. The control surfaces were connected by wires to the operator's hands while he stood below the glider as it hovered in the air. Manipulating these controls, they found their idea of wing warping seemed to be sound. The front elevator when tilted up or down provided control to raise or lower the "nose" of the glider and thus make it rise or come down to earth and land. But that first season, they also learned that there was something terribly wrong with the scientific data they had used in designing the wing. Since this material had come from their idol Lilienthal, they were very depressed. First of all, Lilienthal's figures showed that a glider having the area of wing surface that theirs had should stay aloft in a seventeen miles per hour wind. Their glider would scarcely get off the ground with that wind. They could not, in fact, get the glider off the level ground with a man in it without having two or more men pull the glider down a slope until a much higher wind velocity was produced over the wings.

All experimenters in those early days were dealing with a host of unknown facts. But already it had been discovered that if the top surface of the wing were curved upward near its middle, air passing over what we now call the airfoil created a difference of pressure between the top and bottom surfaces of the wing. This difference provides the lift necessary to sustain a heavier-than-air machine. The faster the wind passes over the wing surface, the greater is the difference of pressure and, consequently, the greater is the lifting force. But another factor enters the situation and that is the so-called "angle of attack" of the wing surface. If the leading edge of the wing is turned upward, wind tends to raise the wing, but there is a loss of lifting force over the upper wing surface. In addition to this there is a shift of the effective lifting force toward the forward edge or back toward the rear of the wing as the angle or wind speed is changed. This shift of the "center of pressure," or position where the entire lifting force can be considered to act, is very important in the design of an airfoil. Lilienthal and other scientists had drawn up tables showing this shift of the center of pressure for various angles the wing made with the oncoming wind and the Wright Brothers followed them faithfully. What was happening was that they were blindly accepting the work of scientists better trained in physics and mathematics than they. As they were discovering, the tables of "scientific" data were very nearly useless.

When Wilbur and Orville returned to Dayton they were not wholly dissatisfied. Their great dissatisfaction was to come in 1901, the next season. They built a larger glider for that season and arranged to leave their business in July so they would have more time to experiment at Kitty Hawk before the autumnal storms made the weather unsuitable for flying. To their discomfiture, however, the larger glider, designed more closely on the data of Lilienthal and other scientists, did not work as well as the small glider built and tested the year before. They spent weeks at Kitty Hawk that summer and built a crude hangar to house the large machine. They worked indefatigably but as they altered the plane to conform to established ideas, they got farther and farther from success. Octave Chanute visited them and gave them unusual encouragement. But the Wrights were depressed. Although they made many glides, the machine still was acting erratically and they could not control it as they wished.

They thought that they had constructed the glider poorly, but Chanute argued that it was as good if not better than other machines and he, being a trained observer, did suggest the heretical thought that perhaps the pressure data might be wrong.

The Wrights returned to Dayton late in August that year and nearly gave up the whole project. If the data were wrong, then all further efforts to design a wing surface that would work were futile. Logically they saw that someone would have to revise the center of pressure tables and that it would require many days and weeks of laborious tests with a crude wind tunnel.

Wind tunnels had been used to test wing surfaces even in that early time. Langley and Lilienthal both had got their data from such testing but they were trained scientists. The Wrights, feeling their lack of such training, were depressed by the formidable task that lay ahead—if they were to go ahead.

Their bicycle business had suffered because of the time they had spent on their gliders; they saw, realistically, no profit to be made by developing a flying machine. In addition, their belief in the ability of men to analyze the problem of flight was profoundly shaken. Wilbur declared that it would be years before the solution could be found.

Had it not been for Chanute, the Wrights might then have relapsed into obscurity. But Chanute continued to encourage them. He wrote and offered his help in the mathematical analysis of wind-tunnel tests. He urged them to build a wind tunnel and go through an exhaustive series of experiments to develop their own data about the all-important "center of pressure." Fortunately, by this time, the Wrights were so badly bitten by the bug of aeronautical science that they could not let go of the problem even though facing it brought an enormous amount of work. That winter, the winter of 1901–02, the Wrights undertook the task of wind-tunnel experimenting and began to assemble the results. In all they tested nearly two hundred wing surfaces. Chanute worked with them, by correspondence, explaining the mathematics, and slowly as the winter months passed, the tables of data grew.

Both the Wrights knew the value of their results—as yet untested but logically sound nonetheless. They recorded their results in notebooks but never published them. As the winter ended, the Wrights recovered their enthusiasm for flying. The bulk of the difficult work of research lay behind them and they were, without knowing it, on the verge of success. They built a new glider, based on the results of the winter's experiments, and eagerly looked forward to a return to Kitty Hawk where they could try out the new machine.

Late in August they started for the sand dunes of the North Carolina coast again. Their new glider, as they altered it in tests that year, became the first successful flying machine. They had added a rudder to the rear of the plane. They made it movable through wire controls handled by the pilot. They also added a rudder to the front of the glider for additional balance and they changed the wingtips. Most of the changes were dictated by the new data they had assembled—and kept secretively in their notebooks.

There was cause for secrecy. Many other scientists and inventors were working on exactly the same problems they were. Chanute, in his letters, urged the Wrights to file for a patent on their plane; he also was most cautious about revealing what he knew of their glider. But perhaps the principal reason for the Wright Brothers' secrecy was the fact that they looked on their glider, on the whole problem of inventing a workable airplane, as a business venture. They had put so much of their time and energy—and their own cash—into the project that they had begun to think of the airplane as a business, not as a scientific accomplishment. Chanute, on the other hand, was primarily interested in the scientific side of the matter.

Octave Chanute and another inventor, Augustus M. Herring, came to Kitty Hawk early in October bringing gliders of Chanute's design. These too were to be tested. They differed from the Wright glider primarily in the method of control. Chanute still was groping for automatic stability in his machines. The Wrights were convinced that the pilot had to bring the plane under control and keep it there—just as a bicycle rider had constantly to exert himself to ride correctly.

Wilbur and Orville had begun to test their machine cautiously and first, as always, as a kite, holding it near the ground and working the control surfaces with wires attached to the glider's wingtips and tail surfaces. When the glider carried a pilot, the plane was kept within a few feet of the ground—sometimes inches from it. For the Wrights were acutely conscious of the danger involved in the tests they were making. Lilienthal as well as other experimenters had been killed. So little was known of the science of aeronautics that extreme caution was certainly called for.

But the Wrights had found success at last. Even after only a few days, they found that their machine responded to the controls almost perfectly. They could raise or lower the nose and wingtips. If a gust pushed a wing down, they could raise it. They had solved the problem of control.

Chanute and Herring left after a very short stay and later in October and on into November the Wrights made hundreds of glides to gain all the experience they could. Since the pilot of their machine had to control it himself, they knew that experience in the art of flying was very important. They wanted to know how to handle the glider as easily as they handled bicycles—automatically correcting changes in flight altitude, moving the controls almost instinctively from hours and days of practice.

As the winter winds grew stronger, they pitted their experience against them and flew in winds as high as thirty-five and more miles per hour. By the time they were ready to return to Dayton and the humdrum bicycle business, they had flown upwards of one thousand times.

When Chanute left earlier that year, he was so sure of the

Wrights' accomplishment that he, with true scientific detachment, told S. P. Langley of the "breakthrough" the Wrights
were making at that time. Langley was perhaps the most
serious rival the Wright Brothers had in the United States. He
too was excited by the information that the Wrights had a
truly workable glider and he telegraphed them, asking permission to come to Kitty Hawk that fall and see what they
had accomplished. But here, the Wright Brothers' innate business conservatism did them a disservice. They were not—and
never were in the future—about to give anything away. In an
understandable way they wanted to protect their investment
and exploit the business potential of their invention. They
also were beginning to feel—indeed had felt for some time—
their lack of rigorous scientific training. They envied scientists
and wanted more than anything to be considered equals in any
dealing with such men as Langley. Yet while Langley was
perfectly willing to accept them as equals, they could not overcome their feelings of inferiority. They replied abruptly to
Langley's request to be permitted to come down that they were
nearly through and there was no more time to experiment. They
packed up, forthwith, and went home to Dayton.

Langley, during that and the following year, was perfecting
a glider of his own design. He had been commissioned by the
government to try to develop a "flying machine" that was
practical, and he believed he had. The next year, 1903, he
planned to test his machine. What Langley lacked in his public
test before crowds and newspapermen was flying experience.
This valuable asset the Wrights had in quantity. They knew
they had a glider now that was nearly perfect in everything
they asked of it. All that remained was to add an engine and a
propeller.

While Langley was readying his machine in the fateful year

of 1903, the Wrights were struggling with the problems of a light engine and the mysteries of propeller design. Their only source of information on propellers lay in the files of ship and ship-propulsion experts. But the problems of designing a propeller for motion through the air were quite different from those for motion through water. The Wrights, in fact, discovered that there was no theory of propellers. Marine engineers used the simple "cut and try" method to develop a marine propeller that would answer their requirements. Once again the Wrights were forced by circumstance to turn themselves into scientists. When they were through testing and studying propellers, they knew more about them than anyone in the world. Thus they were already far ahead of all rivals. They possessed the only accurate knowledge of the theory of airfoils and the most advanced knowledge of propellers.

For an engine, the Wrights at first cast about among gasoline engine manufacturers, hoping they could find a company that would undertake the job. The requirements they set forth were that the engine should develop at least eight horsepower and not weigh more than 20 pounds per horsepower, or 160 pounds. They did not specify that the engine was going to power a "flying machine" but even so they were unable to find a company that would take the contract. The result was that the Wrights had to build their own. They produced one that developed between twelve and sixteen horsepower. It weighed only 170 pounds.

The engine was to be linked to the propeller by means of a chain drive similar in action to that of a bicycle chain. At first the Wrights planned to use only one propeller, but later they introduced a second one turning opposite to the first to counterbalance the effects of the propeller rotation or torque.

All elements had been worked out. All theory—as far as

theory went—pointed to success. The gliding experience gained in 1902 made both Wilbur and Orville confident they could manage the flying machine once it was in the air. Near the end of September, 1903, they started enthusiastically for Kitty Hawk. In all the world at that time there were no more than three people who believed the Wrights might fly. The Wrights, of course, were confident, and Chanute was giving them his usual encouragement. But with his scientific detachment he could not share the emotional conviction they had that this time they would realize man's ancient dream of flight.

On their arrival at Kitty Hawk the Wrights found that their glider hangar was in bad repair. They set to work rebuilding it and then built another hangar nearby. Their 1902 glider was there and during the weeks of preparation both men took turns "getting their hand in" at more gliding experience in the old machine.

When they put the new machine together and mounted the engine, they were aiming at a test flight early in November. But on the first trial of the engine, it backfired twisting one of the propeller shafts as well as rupturing the propeller support. Both shafts were sent back to Dayton to be refashioned from stronger metal. Octave Chanute came to visit and witness the proposed tests but the weather already was turning cold and blustery. Chanute stayed a week and then left.

Orville Wright had taken the shafts back to Dayton for rebuilding and on his return to the isolated station at Kitty Hawk he brought the news that Langley's machine had failed for the second time in a public test. Both brothers felt a mixture of elation and sadness at the news. Naturally they wanted to win the prize of being the first to fly and their elation over Langley's failure was understandable. But they were saddened by the ridicule the newspapers heaped on Langley. For they, of all people in the world, knew best the number of problems facing anyone attempting to "do the impossible" and fly. In reading later reports of the Langley failure, the Wrights and all other knowledgeable aeronauts saw that the launching system devised by Langley had not performed as it was designed and so no true test of his airplane's design in flight could follow. But this made no difference to reporters covering the event. They saw only comic failure and wrote their stories accordingly.

Delay after delay plagued the Wright Brothers at Kitty Hawk. November was well along before they discovered that they could not fasten the sprockets to the shaft mountings securely. The engine vibrated so much that the nuts would not stay tightly fastened to the securing bolts. While this may not appear to be a major difficulty, it must be remembered that the Wrights were far away from their shop with its machines and tools. And any minor difficulty could be as disastrous to their plans as a major one if it prevented perfect operation.

Clearly they would have to improvise—and since improvising was what they had been doing for years on their gliders, they characteristically solved the problem. They used bicycle cement on the bolt threads and after melting some of it on the bolts and nuts they tightened them, permanently. But now with everything in mechanical readiness, the weather began to deteriorate. They had already been through what must have been a minor hurricane. Winds of 75 miles per hour had threatened to blow away machines, hangars, camp and all. But now, day after day, it was either raining or snowing. The wind either was too strong to attempt a flight or the day was absolutely windless. Of course if the Wrights had had a long level field and wheels on their machine, they could have flown on a windless day. But they had yet to put wheels on the airplane. They had, instead, long runners acting as skids to ease the plane on landings. For launching they had built a sixty-foot track. A small wheeled cart ran on the track and the plane was mounted on the cart. The usual system for launching a glider from this was for two people to stand at the wingtips and move the glider forward until enough lift was developed over the wing surfaces for the glider to rise. This meant of course that some wind had to be blowing because two men could not move a glider fast enough in a sixty-foot run to develop lift enough to get it airborne.

When testing the engine on November 28 they discovered one of the rebuilt propeller shafts had developed a crack. Orville rushed back to Dayton to get new shafts. He returned on December 11. With the new shafts in place the Wrights waited impatiently for wind.

During all their tests they had become acquainted with the men operating the life-saving station at Kill Devil Hill about a mile away from their camp. These men, somewhat skeptical but interested in the Wrights' experiments, wanted to be on hand when the first attempt was made. The Wrights agreed that they would display a signal on one of their hangars which would be visible from the distant station when they were ready to fly.

On December 14 they hoisted it. There still was no wind but they were tired of waiting and they were going to drag the plane and its track to a hillside where they hoped they could develop sufficient speed to get the plane off the ground by running it downhill.

When the men at the station saw the signal they hurried over and helped the Wrights drag the 750-pound machine to the hillside. With the plane in place on the track, Wilbur and Orville flipped a coin to see who would be first to try. Wilbur won.

After he had settled himself in the plane and warmed up the engine, Wilbur released the holding wire and Orville ran forward with the plane as it moved. But it moved faster than either of them had anticipated. About two-thirds of the way down the track it rose into the air and left Orville behind. The plane nosed up swiftly, too far. It stalled and came down on the ground, damaging the left wingtip and one of the landing skids.

Neither brother was discouraged. They spent the next two days repairing the plane and waiting for a moderate wind. But the winter winds were strong, boisterous and gusty. On the night of December 16, both Orville and Wilbur decided that whatever the weather they would try a flight on the 17th. It was well past their usual schedule for flying. The bicycle business had been abandoned much too long. And the two brothers wanted to be home for Christmas.

That night as they lay in their cots, they heard a strong cold wind blowing from the north. When they rose the next morning, they looked out on the bleak dunes. Wind whistled by the hangars and the puddles of rain water had a skim of ice over them. They breakfasted and then waited, hoping the wind would die down. But it continued to blow gusty and cold at from 22 to 27 miles per hour. At ten o'clock they decided to wait no more. They hung up the signal once again and set about readying the plane. They faced it into the wind on level ground, feeling that with such a wind they certainly could make a flight from a horizontal track. Several men arrived from the life-saving station.

Orville got in the plane and started the engine. He waited a few minutes until it had warmed up and then, with Wilbur holding a wing, released the wire brake. The plane moved slowly in the high wind and Wilbur easily stayed with it. As on the previous occasion, the plane rose into the air about 40 feet from its starting point. As it did, one of the men from the life-saving station snapped the shutter of a camera the Wrights had positioned beforehand. It shows the plane only a couple of feet off the ground but it is the photographic record of the first powered airplane flight in the history of the world.

In the gusty wind the plane behaved erratically and Orville had difficulty controlling it. He found the front elevator to be extremely delicate so that when he altered its angle only a little the plane rose or fell with alarming speed. Orville struggled with the controls but he depressed the elevator too much on one occasion and the plane "landed" abruptly. It was not damaged, although Orville had not intended to land so soon. The flight lasted only twelve seconds. With the relative wind velocity, they calculated that the actual 120 feet of powered flight through the air was equivalent to a distance of 540 feet in calm air.

With characteristic energy they hauled the plane back to the track and Wilbur tried a flight. His results were about the same as Orville's. On Orville's next trial flight he stayed aloft fifteen seconds and traveled 200 feet. At noon Wilbur began the fourth flight. He got off the ground and had the same difficulty Orville experienced controlling the elevator of the plane. He swooped up and down, then brought it under control so that for a while he was flying smoothly; then he began the swooping motion again. The plane struck the ground 852 feet from its take-off point after a flight of 59 seconds.

The brothers were elated. The spectators—who doubled as assistants in hauling the machine to the track—were not quite sure what they had witnessed. As they gathered around the plane and Wilbur climbed out of it, they began talking about the flight, its duration and the distance covered. Then a great gust of wind picked the plane up and turned it over and over, rolling it along the dunes. The men clung to it as best they could, but it suffered serious damage and could not be flown again immediately.

Whether or not the spectators knew the importance of that day, the Wrights certainly did. They knew the problem of flight had been solved. That afternoon they walked to the weather station some five miles away and sent a telegram to their father saying "Success four flights Thursday morning against twenty-one-mile wind started from level with engine power alone average speed thirty-one miles longest fifty seconds inform press home Christmas."

Orville signed it.

Viewed today, what followed that announcement takes on a comic aspect. The message was relayed to Norfolk where a reporter from the *Virginian-Pilot* got hold of it and wrote up a story. In it he said that the machine had a six-bladed propeller underneath to "elevate" it, another propeller to drive it forward and that, among other things, the flight had covered three miles.

The news had been given to the reporter by the Norfolk telegraph operator specifically against the wishes of the Wrights. They wanted to make the announcement themselves and they wanted the facts to be straight. But the cat, so to speak, was out of the bag. The Norfolk paper offered the story to a total of 21 newspapers. Only five reported it—if reported is the correct word. The stories were garbled and based on no exact information at all. Of the five papers that took the story, only one besides the Norfolk paper gave it immediate coverage on the front page and that paper was the Cincinnati *Enquirer*. Since the *Virginian-Pilot,* the Norfolk paper, was a member of the Associated Press, the story was available to all member papers. But even the Dayton *Journal* failed to use it.

As the days passed, more and more papers printed the story, or some form of it. Most editors did not believe human flight was possible in anything but a gas-filled balloon and many confused the Wrights' flight with such balloon flights as were then common enough in both Europe and the United States.

In Dayton, the Wrights prepared a careful story and released it to the press in an attempt to get some semblance of accuracy concerning their accomplishment. But the press of the United States refused to be "taken in" by any claims so fantastic. In this way the age of flight came to the world.

Between that fateful day in 1903 and the present, the entire world has changed. Much of that change can be traced to the invention of the first flying machine. It did not, of course, spring overnight into the great airliners of the present. The Wrights themselves worked the remainder of their lives on the development of the planes. Not a little of their time was spent defending their claim of priority and demonstrating their machines both in the United States and in Europe. For a time they actually controlled the manufacture of airplanes through their patents. But a discovery as important and as far reaching as theirs could not remain for long in the hands of any group.

Military men the world over recognized the importance of the airplane and as more powerful engines were developed and the science of aeronautics grew, planes began to be true transports of both goods and people. Today any point on the face of the earth is a matter of hours away from any other point. The travel between continents and nations has shrunk the globe—presenting statesmen and businessmen with problems never dreamed of before.

Controversy and ignorance surrounded the Wrights for many years after their first flight. Their desire for secrecy did not help. They continued to work alone, unaided by any outside funds. Correctly or otherwise, they felt they did not reap the benefits their long years of work entitled them to, although the world and their country did honor them.

In 1912 Wilbur Wright contracted typhoid fever. He died on May 30 of that year. Orville lived on alone. The two brothers had been close all their lives and neither had married. Orville saw the air age come to the world. He died at the age of seventy-seven in 1948.

The two of them are remembered as one. Their accomplishment has become legend—a legend of two quiet men, who ran a bicycle shop in Dayton, Ohio.

Ernest Rutherford:
Midwife to the Atomic Age

"What the atom of each element is, whether it is a movement, or a thing, or a vortex, or a point having inertia, whether there is any limit to its divisibility and, if so, how that limit is imposed, whether the long list of elements is final, or whether any of them have a common origin, all these questions remain surrounded by a darkness as profound as ever."

This statement, made during the last decade of the nineteenth century, gives us today a clue to the situation then existing in atomic science. It was made by Lord Salisbury in a speech in 1894 to the British Association.

Ask any schoolboy today what an atom looks like and, thinking he knows, he'll tell you. He also will tell you it can be divided, that new elements can be formed from other, known, elements. He knows of radioactivity and of atomic explosions, controlled reactions and nuclear power plants. He knows because he is a product of what we frequently call the "atomic age." What this schoolboy does know about atoms was discovered during the past 65 years, and one of the outstanding contributors to our present acquaintance with the atom was Lord Rutherford of Nelson.

He was one of the first scientists to observe the natural disintegration of radioactive elements.

He gave the scientific world its first partially accurate "picture" or idea of what an atom looked like.

He was first to transmute elements by particle bombardment turning nitrogen into oxygen.

He acquired this new knowledge and formed all his deductions from experimental work in his laboratory.

If atoms were the size of croquet balls, they would have been observed and described long ago. And one of the reasons Rutherford's work was so strikingly original in experimental approach was, of course, that atoms are invisible. The question naturally rises: How can one experiment with invisible particles? How can one even suspect, much less know, they are actually present in a container or a glass tube?

The situation in atomic science when Rutherford began his researches is well put by Lord Salisbury's statement. But a simpler way of understanding the problem facing men of Rutherford's time is with a rudimentary experiment. Take eight or ten identical cigar boxes. Have someone place various objects in each one; for example, a wad of cotton in one, twenty small ball bearings in another, four wooden matches in a third, and so on. Have the person loading the boxes seal them tightly and hand them to you one at a time. Your problem: Describe what is in each box without opening it. You can shake the boxes, weigh them, listen to whatever goes on inside when they are shaken. *But you cannot open them and see what is inside.*

This, crudely, is the kind of problem that faced Ernest Rutherford and his colleagues in those early, exciting and fruitful days of atomic research.

Ernest Rutherford was born in New Zealand in 1871 of pioneering parents. His father was of Scottish descent; his mother came from Sussex, England. They lived during Rutherford's earliest years in a crude pioneer cottage of few and small rooms. Ernest Rutherford's father processed flax, cut wood and farmed to support his family, and the young boy's daily life was typical of that of any farm boy of the region. As he grew, he fished and hunted with his brothers and friends. On occasion he was ordered to tutor his younger sisters in their schoolwork and he displayed a certain touch of genius in organization of his subjects: he kept the girls in place and more or less under his thumb by tying their pigtails together.

His own schooling he received in the new free public schools established in the new country, and he devoured knowledge insatiably. Whatever the caliber of the instruction, Rutherford got the most from his lessons—so much that he won a scholarship to Nelson College, where he went at the age of sixteen to begin serious preparation for his future.

Nelson College itself was not pretentious but Rutherford's developing interest in science and mathematics brought him into contact with a young instructor, Mr. Littlejohn, whose classes were so badly attended that frequently he had only Rutherford for a student. It amounted to having a private tutor and Rutherford took advantage of that situation. From Nelson College, he won a scholarship to Canterbury College, which then was a young institution with only seven professors and about 150 students.

While he was at Canterbury, Rutherford undertook the first serious research of his long life. He had become interested in "Hertzian waves," as they were then called, their production and reception. Today we call them radio waves and "know all about them." But in Rutherford's youth they were mysterious, exciting, and little was known concerning them. This led him to experiment and to the exploration of a little-known area of science. It also led him to England, to Cambridge University and to the world-famous Cavendish Laboratory where his life-work truly began.

In 1895 the Cavendish Laboratory was under the direction of J. J. Thomson. Along the walks nearby and on the green lawns students of outstanding ability, and/or unquestioned wealth and background, strolled casually on the summer day that Rutherford arrived. He seemed older than the undergraduates (he was) and younger than the dons (he was). Gradually it dawned on the undergraduates that there were a number of young men about the campus who didn't quite seem to fit into the scheme of things at Cambridge. That is, they didn't *look* like university men. They weren't. They were the first product of a plan to offer research grants to able graduate students from the colonies, and it was no wonder that the first crop didn't have the look or manner of sophisticated young Harrovians or Etonians.

Rutherford was the first of the "outlanders" to arrive on the campus and he promptly enrolled at "The Cavendish," as the world-famous laboratory was called. To the undergraduates of Cambridge, Rutherford looked the part of a colonial rube. He was large, well over six feet, and had a big-boned athletic body. His face was ruddy, open and inquiring, almost shame-lessly eager—all of which are serious faults to a sophisticate. As other students arrived, registered and began work at the Cavendish they all underwent inspection by the professors, by the undergraduates and by each other. From the very beginning Rutherford gave the almost universal impression of a genuine person, free from guile, a man with a hearty laugh—a man who liked a good joke. But was he a good scientist?

A few weeks of work answered that question. So great were Rutherford's powers of concentration that he could study in a room full of noise. Legend has it that if he were deep in thought or reading, he could be playfully struck on the head and not even be aware of it. And he showed from the start an enormous imagination and ingenuity in asking penetrating questions and designing experimental equipment to help answer them.

In this regard he was better fitted than Sir J. J. Thomson himself. For Thomson, a brilliant scientist, was all thumbs with equipment in the laboratory, so much so that when his assistants brought in very thin-walled glass tubes for an experiment, they tried to keep Thomson away from them—somehow the man always managed to break the apparatus. Aside from this drawback, however, Thomson was the best man in the British Empire under whom Rutherford could work.

Thomson had been appointed head of The Cavendish in 1884 when he was only twenty-eight years old and for years had been convinced that major natural secrets could be discovered by studying the effect of electrical discharges through gases. Sir William Crookes had developed a tube of gas under low pressure which emitted a glow when high voltages were applied at the metal electrodes at each end.

Contrary to German research theories, Crookes believed the glow or ray of light reaching from one end of the tube to the other under a particular vacuum was made up of electrically charged particles of matter. The German theory held that it was entirely a wave phenomenon. If the light was made up of charged particles it should be deflected by an adjacent electric field or a magnet. But researchers were unable to detect any deflection of the beam. Hence the Germans stuck to the wave theory of the occurrence.

Thomson, after years of work, managed to produce deflection, calculate the size of the particles and their velocities. The astonishing fact was that he had discovered a particle nearly 2000 times smaller than the smallest and lightest known atom (hydrogen). He had, in fact, discovered the electron.

It was into this exciting phase of developments that Rutherford stepped in 1895. Exciting, but at times frustrating, for The Cavendish, while being the center of British research in physics, was also operating on a budget which today would be laughed out of a good high school. If as much as five pounds were needed for a piece of apparatus, long, detailed discussions were begun, more profound thought went into alternative courses of action before the money was spent. So strict was the budget that The Cavendish was nicknamed the "string and sealing wax" laboratory. Many of the researchers used cardboard, tin cans and plenty of string and sealing wax to build their own apparatus.

There were other drawbacks to Thomson's laborious researches. For one thing, extremely high voltages were needed to get the gases under test to conduct a current and show their character for measurement and examination. The only way to produce these voltages was to string together a multitude of storage batteries of crude design. The resulting voltage created very high temperatures and frequently stray discharges to nearby objects interrupted observations. To make matters worse, the batteries ran down rapidly and constantly had to be recharged. Another great drawback was the problem of creating a vacuum in the tube. The pumps available then in The Cavendish were very weak. They had to be run continuously for several hours before a sufficient vacuum was created in the sealed glass tubes for discharge to take place. Today a modestly priced pump will create a sufficient vacuum within minutes. Despite all these drawbacks, however, Thomson, Rutherford and the other researchers worked enthusiastically on what were then the very outer limits of science.

They were not alone. In Germany and in France researchers were equally busy pursuing similar investigation. Some worked on the analysis of various colors produced by glowing gases, others worked with such elements as uranium, still others pursued the same line Thomson was on: investigation of electrical discharges through gases under low pressure.

Another scientist, Wilhelm Conrad Roentgen, was working with such discharges through various gases and made one of the great accidental discoveries of science. He had in his laboratory a screen coated with barium platinocyanide which he normally used to detect wave lengths of emitted light outside the range of human vision. He moved it, one day, near the tube of gas through which a discharge was taking place and to his amazement, it fluoresced brightly. Inadvertently he put his hand between the tube and the screen and to his complete astonishment he saw not only the shadow of his hand but the entire bone structure. The shadow of the flesh of his hand was light, the skeletal structure was dark. He had discovered what we today call X-rays. Roentgen made exhaustive experiments with his newly discovered emanations, telling no one of his discovery, not even his wife. He found the rays would fog photographic plates even though the plates were wrapped in many thicknesses of paper. More important to Thomson and Rutherford in England was the fact that these rays would make any gas in a tube conduct electricity with only a few volts applied at the electrodes. When Roentgen announced his discovery in 1895, both Thomson and Rutherford knew the way had been cleared for them to carry on further investigation far more rapidly than had been possible before.

Announcement of the discovery of Roentgen rays, as they first were called, produced an equally strong effect on the public, a quite different one from that on Thomson and Rutherford.

The penetrating power of the rays alarmed the ladies of the day. Entrepreneurs quickly brought out "ray-proof" undergarments for the panicky ladies. Any man who gazed through opera glasses too long at a neighboring lady opera-goer was believed to be immodestly using the Roentgen rays. And a current bit of doggerel went the rounds:

> I hear they'll gaze through cloak and gown—and
>> even stays
> Those naughty, naughty Roentgen rays.

Typically, the public had been misinformed. But the penetrating power of the X-rays was quickly used by the medical profession to examine bone fractures and to locate metal objects inadvertently swallowed by their patients.

In 1896 another great chance discovery by Antoine Henri Becquerel in France gave all scientists yet another mystery to unravel. In experimenting with uranium salts and spurred by the great furor over X-rays, Becquerel wondered whether all phosphorescent materials might not produce mysterious rays. Accordingly he placed some uranium salt atop a photographic plate wrapped in paper. Beneath the paper he placed an aluminum disk. When he developed the plate several days later, he found a picture of the disk on the plate. Clearly, the uranium salt was emitting something that affected a photographic plate. And it was doing so spontaneously. Becquerel named the phenomenon radioactivity and his announcement set Marie Curie on her long road to the discovery of radium as one of the naturally radioactive elements.

The discovery affected Rutherford differently. He had worked with Thomson and seen the discovery of a particle of matter smaller than the smallest known atom. Its electrical charge had been measured. Its velocity had been computed. It was known to be negatively charged. Roentgen's X-rays remained as mysterious and as powerful as ever. Now Becquerel had some compounds of uranium which seemed to be emitting particles naturally, without men doing anything to them. Were they atoms? Or parts of atoms? *What was an atom, anyway?*

Thomson had his own idea of what an atom would look like if he could see it. He conceived it to be a small sphere of matter, the matter having an over-all positive charge. In this sphere were embedded small particles having a negative charge, i.e., electrons. If sufficient energy were used, some of these electrons could be plucked out of the sphere and set free. These free electrons, under the influence of a properly arranged electric field, would form a so-called cathode ray in a partially evacuated tube. The atoms from which electrons were taken gained in positive charge (by the removal of negatively charged electrons) and so were said to be ionized. Some electrons struck and held to other atoms, thus producing negative ions. It was an ingenious idea but it failed to answer one important test in the laboratory. When streams of electrons were "fired" at a very thin metal sheet of gold or platinum foil, some of the electrons passed right on through, which they could not do if the atoms were "solid spheres" as Thomson visualized them. As a matter of fact this ability of electrons to proceed right on through dense metals such as gold helped persuade German scientists that the cathode rays, or streams of electrons, were actually electromagnetic waves rather than particles.

The idea of an atom being the ultimate particle of matter was as old as Democritus, the Epicurean Greek philosopher. But his and later concepts were merely that—ideas, not testable realities. There is an ancient drawing of one concept of atoms showing small solid spheres linked to each other with several fishhook-like extensions. The hooked extensions, of course, held matter together and the central spheres were indivisible ultimate particles.

Earlier in the nineteenth century, Dalton, the English chemist, Berzelius, the Swedish chemist, and Avogadro, an Italian, among many others were at work on their theories of the atom. But they were specifically interested in answering chemical questions through the use of their ideas of what an ultimate particle was. Although much useful work was done chemically, little or nothing was done to track down the exact nature, size and form of that smallest particle, the atom.

Rutherford, then, came on the scene during a period of great activity and discovery. He soaked up all the latest information from other research centers, pondered all the admissible experimental evidence and continued to gather more of it in the laboratory at Cambridge.

With Becquerel's announcement of radioactivity, many scientists began examining the emanations. One of the earliest experiments devised was to take a tray of uranium salt and place it near the poles of a magnet. Beyond the magnet was placed a photographic plate. As the particles sprang spontaneously from the uranium, some of them sped between the poles of the magnet and went on until they struck the photographic plate. When the plate was developed, the points where the particles struck it were clearly marked.

Examining these positions, Rutherford quickly saw that one kind of particle was deflected a great amount from its straight path on passing through the magnetic field. Still another particle was deflected a lesser amount but in the opposite direction. He concluded that these particles bore opposite electrical charges, since they reacted oppositely in the magnetic field. According to Faraday's and Maxwell's principles of electromagnetism, Rutherford identified the least deflected particle as positive, the other as negative. It also appeared clear to Rutherford that the particles that were bent the least distance from their path on passing through the magnetic field were substantially larger, more massive particles than the other ones which were turned from their path through a comparatively large distance before striking the plate.

Knowing nothing of their nature beyond the charge and relative sizes of them, Rutherford named them Alpha and Beta particles. Streams of them coming from radioactive materials were termed Alpha and Beta rays. Later, when different radioactive compounds were used, a third type of radiation was discovered which was not deflected by the magnetic field at all. Because of this, it was assumed that the third type of emanation was electrically neutral. It was called Gamma radiation.

Further investigation by Rutherford led him to believe that the Beta radiation was a stream of high velocity electrons. What the Alpha particles were he did not yet know, but he was determined to find out.

At the time of identifying the Alpha and Beta rays Ernest Rutherford was twenty-eight years old. He was J. J. Thomson's outstanding "pupil" at The Cavendish, and when McGill University in Montreal wrote Thomson asking that he recommend someone to run their physics laboratory, he could do little else but recommend his protégé. Rutherford went to McGill, and there he shortly was joined by another outstanding researcher, Frederick Soddy, who was twenty-three years old.

As head of the experimental work at McGill, Rutherford and his team of researchers produced scores of papers announcing results of their experiments which quite literally shook the scientific world. Still on the track of identifying the Alpha particles, Rutherford devised experiments which eventually led to the discovery of their true nature. In an elaborate series of tests, Rutherford's researchers isolated an invisible and capricious "emanation," as they called it. It was first detected in the laboratory during the examination of the radioactive element thorium. The radiation-sensing instrument of the time was a simple electroscope, and it was found that this instrument was disturbed when someone opened the door of the laboratory and a draft of air swept by the apparatus. By collecting this "emanation" from the radiating thorium in a glass tube over a period of time, Rutherford eventually showed that what was being produced from the thorium was the element helium. While this was a major discovery in itself it heralded another and even more upsetting discovery: that certain natural elements, the radioactive ones, were spontaneously decaying. They were breaking down at a measurable rate and the entire theory of an immutable atom fell to the ground.

In the span of a few short years at McGill, Rutherford and his co-workers determined the rate of decay of various elements and coined the presently used term "half-life" of radioactive materials. If, for example, an element loses half of its radioactivity in, say, four days, it will lose half its remaining "life" in another four days, and half of the remaining life in yet another, until it has become "dead" as far as spontaneous disintegration is concerned.

Today it is difficult to imagine the consternation which Rutherford's announcement caused among scientists. The chemists, for example, had built the entire structure of their science on the presumed immutability of the atom. Physicists had counted heavily on the indestructibility of matter and, in fact, one of the sacred beliefs was that matter could be neither created nor destroyed. Yet here, according to Rutherford, were natural elements in the process, apparently, of destroying themselves.

During the first years of the twentieth century, Rutherford's experimental work laid the groundwork for still further attacks on the atom—with Rutherford happily in the van. By the time he completed his major work at McGill, he had the ability to assess young research people and he was rarely wrong in his assessment. He had the uncanny, unexplainable ability to suggest a way to approach a problem which would lead to its solution. He knew more about the small particles called ions than any man alive. Indeed he had become almost sentimental about them, referring to them as "jolly little beggars." Frequently he expressed sorrow for other people who, as he put it, "hadn't labs to work in."

Unlike the popular conception of research scientists, Rutherford was a congenial, outgoing person and a keen student of psychology. Knowing that if he "popped in" unannounced on his researchers in the various rooms, he would probably find some of them loafing, he would approach the rooms whistling loudly to forewarn the inhabitants of his coming. He had a rare quality for a leader: the ability to mingle socially with his assistants, to appear as an equal with younger, less brilliant men and at the same time command their respect and draw from them their best work. His devotion to physics was singular, and he once remarked "All science is either physics or stamp collecting." And while the remark is not wholly true it is not entirely false either. For in his work, already accomplished and yet to come, Rutherford showed that the understanding of the fundamental laws and constituents of the physical universe would come through physics.

Rutherford had an important qualification for a great experimenter: a healthy skepticism of unsupported theory. In this he was temperamentally different from his German counterparts. For many of them loved a bold theory, an imaginative projection of their human egos into a grand "scheme" of things that would explain much that was as yet unknown. As it happens, both approaches to science can be useful. So men like Rutherford temper the imaginative flights of others; while sometimes the imaginative flight, the bold theory, pays off.

One such bold theory was Einstein's first public announcement in 1905 of the now accepted Theory of Relativity. When Einstein published his first form of the theory, it roused a great deal of discussion both inside and outside of scientific circles. It was, and still is, difficult to grasp because it apparently refutes accepted ideas of time and space and motion. When it was first published, Rutherford remarked to one of his young co-workers, 'I don't suppose there are half a dozen men in the world who understand it." And when the student asked respectfully who the other five men were, Rutherford roared with laughter and said, "You don't believe I understand it, do you?" At another time, Rutherford showed his skepticism of theory when a continental scientist said to him, "No Anglo-Saxon can understand relativity." Rutherford replied, "No, they have too much sense."

We know today that the testable aspects of Einstein's theory have supported it. And we also know that in forming it, Einstein made one of the great contributions of all time to science. His genius lay in theory. Rutherford's lay in the laboratory where, given observations of a series of experiments, he could deduce the correct answer to a question. It was genius of a different kind but not of a different order from Einstein's. More clearly than any man before him, Rutherford was beginning to "see" the invisible atom.

One of the great problems facing any experimenter is the one of inventing equipment to do the desired job. Both Isaac Newton and Galileo Galilei were ingenious and dextrous enough to invent and build their own. As an experimenter of the first rank, Rutherford and his contemporaries had to do the same. Sir William Crookes developed one such instrument which we today call the scintillator. It consisted simply of a metal plate coated with zinc sulfide which, when placed in a darkened chamber and struck by an Alpha particle, would fluoresce at the spot of impact. By observing the screen through a telescope, any researcher could count the number of scintillations and know the rate of emission of particles from a sample of radioactive material.

Another more widely known device to detect radiation was developed by Rutherford and a research assistant. It consisted of a hollow metal cylinder with a wire stretched tight down the middle of the tube. A high voltage was applied to the tube and wire, and the space between them occupied by a gas. When an Alpha particle entered the tube, it ionized the gas and provided a circuit from wire to tube. There was a momentary discharge which could be used to operate a light bulb or a sounding device. Today we know this as the Geiger counter, for Rutherford's research assistant was Hans Geiger.

This device was perfected after Rutherford left McGill University to accept the post of Langworthy Professor of Physics at Manchester University in England. It was here that Rutherford set a young research assistant to work on what was to be the most important experiment of his long, experiment-filled life.

It had been noticed by many scientists that Beta particles could penetrate dense metals such as gold or platinum or lead. When a stream of these particles was aimed at a sheet of such metal, many of them passed through as though the dense metal sheet did not exist. When Alpha particles were fired at such metal foil, they too passed on through. It also was noticed that Beta particles were scattered on passing through, that they were diverted from their paths. Since some care was taken to focus the stream of Beta particles, the conclusion was that they were diverted by the atoms of the foil. Alpha particles responded in the same way but were diverted less because they had a much greater mass than the Beta particles and were therefore harder to deflect.

Obviously J. J. Thomson's idea of what the atom "looked like" could not account for either the passage of the particles through the foil or the scattering effect. At Manchester, Rutherford discussed a research problem with Hans Geiger. He had on his staff at the time a young student and he wanted to get him to work on a project. Rutherford agreed with Geiger that the student was ready to go to work on something new, and so it was agreed that young Ernest Marsden would attempt to scatter Alpha particles through a large angle—a feat which Rutherford did not believe could be done.

The equipment was not elaborate. It consisted of a sheet of gold foil 4/100,000 of a centimeter thick, a source of Alpha particles focused on the "target" of the foil, a telescope and an adjustable scintillator beyond the foil. The scintillator could be placed at any desired angle to the direction of the beam of Alpha particles, and the impacts of diverted Alpha particles observed with the telescope. In a sense, Marsden was set to work merely counting bright flashes of light striking the zinc sulfide screen of the scintillator. He would place the scintillator at some angle—say five degrees—to the stream of particles and note the number of impacts on the screen there. Then move the screen to another position and resume counting.

Until Marsden ran this experiment, it was believed that the scattering of Alpha and Beta particles was caused by a series of collisions in the foil between particles and atoms of the foil. Since a particle had as much chance of being diverted to the

right as to the left upon a chance collision, the net change of
the particle's directions after the series of supposed collisions
probably would not be great. It might, for example, strike
eight atoms so as to send it to the right and ten so as to send
it to the left. The net change would be slightly to the left of
its original path. In such a situation the laws of probability
apply and the number of particles diverted by any great angle
is extremely small—particularly Alpha particles, which are
relatively massive and difficult to divert. Geiger had in fact
calculated the average angle of deflection for Alpha particles,
using the laws of probability, and come up with the figure of
0.87 degrees—less than a degree deflection. What hope, then,
of finding any Alpha particles diverted through an angle of
90 degrees? Practically none.

So Marsden set to work on the project devised by Rutherford.
Painstakingly he noted the number of scintillations when the
counter was set at various angles. Gradually he increased the
angle between the recording instrument and the stream of
Alpha particles. The number of scintillations recorded at larger
and larger angles decreased as was expected. But when he got
to an angle of 90 degrees and peered through the telescope at
the screen of the scintillator, he saw an occasional tiny burst of
light indicating that, contrary to expectations, some Alpha
particles were diverted through an angle of 90 degrees.

This was so contrary to the deductions made from previous
knowledge that when he tried to explain the results of the
experiment, Rutherford declared that it was like firing a fif-
teen-inch shell at a piece of tissue paper and having the shell
bounce back and hit you.

At the time of the experiment, Rutherford knew more about
the nature of small particles and their handling than anyone
in the world. He had as clear an idea of what the atom looked

like as anyone else—and it was not a very clear idea. The results of this single experiment told him that the idea was not accurate and for one year he kept probing, searching and thinking, trying to explain the 90-degree deflection of the Alpha particles. Of one thing he began to be certain, the deflection of particles passing through the thin sheets of foil was not due to a series of chance collisions with atoms. Too many particles were passing straight through, and those that were diverted through large angles defied the laws of probability and all calculations using a series of collisions as a starting point.

He saw clearly that he would have to abandon Thomson's concept, which held that the atom was a sphere of positive charge with electrons embedded in it. The diverted Alpha particles were acting exactly as though they were deflected by a single collision with or approach to an extremely small, powerful positive charge, a charge that could be thought of as concentrated at a point. If, Rutherford reasoned, each atom is electrically neutral, which it is, and all the positive charge is concentrated at a point, then where is the negative charge? Though small, the atom was much larger than the point of positive charge, and Rutherford began to believe that the negatively charged electrons of the atom were at a considerable distance from the positive point charge. This, he reasoned, would account for high-speed electrons passing through the atoms of gold in the foil. They must have gone through the space between the positive point charge and the more distant electrons of the atom. It might be, he believed, very much like our solar system. The earth and other planets could be thought of as electrons, a great distance from the central sun, which would be the positive charge at the middle.

This idea of Rutherford's, of likening the atom to our solar system, displayed his genius for thinking of science in physical rather than theoretical, abstract terms. He knew, even as he thought of this "model" of the atom, that there were serious drawbacks to it. It left many questions unanswered but it did answer some very disturbing questions. It explained the scattering Alpha particles as no other model could do. Rutherford gave the name "nucleus" to the very small positive point charge at the center of the atom, and he immediately set Geiger and Marsden to work on an experiment to check his model for accuracy.

If his model were closer to a true picture of what the atom looks like than any previous one, and if his assumption that the Alpha particle was diverted by a single collision with or approach to this nucleus, then, according to calculation, the particles should describe hyperbolic paths as they sped through the field of the atom. Geiger and Marsden again set to work on the scintillator and made a count of over 100,000 scintillations. When they were through and had assessed their results, they concluded that Rutherford's model was essentially correct.

The radius of the nucleus, according to Rutherford, was about 0.000000000003 centimeters while the radius of the entire atom was 0.00000001 centimeters.

Other scientists were quick to point out that the Rutherford model of the atom contradicted certain known electrical laws. If, they asked, the electrons were circling the positive nucleus, why did not the electrons, being attracted to positive charges, fall into the nucleus, thus destroying the atom? Rutherford cheerfully admitted his atom was "self-destroying" but, he maintained, it worked. It answered questions. As to why the atom did not destroy itself, he did not know.

But he felt certain that further research would disclose the reason.

Rutherford's belief in research, in experiment, was boundless and he did not let apparent contradictions dismay him. He had, at this time, some of the outstanding young scientists in the world working with him. His fame was worldwide and in 1919 he was invited to accept the position of head of The Cavendish Laboratory where he had begun his lifework as a research student years before. He accepted the post and held it until his death in 1937.

The speed with which atomic science developed during the latter part of Rutherford's life is astonishing when it is viewed against the relatively slow progress of science through the centuries before. One of the reasons for the great unfolding of atomic mysteries in the course of less than half a century was the dogged, experimental determination of Ernest Rutherford. Fortunately for science, he frequently had many brilliant research students working on projects he had devised and so he accomplished much more than he could have done alone. Many of these students became world-famous in their own right due to discoveries made during and after their direct association with Rutherford.

Among the outstanding of these was H. G. Moseley who, through spectroscopic analysis, gave chemists the orderly periodic table we use today. By arranging elements according to the size of the positive charge on the nucleus rather than by atomic weight, Moseley "straightened out" the periodic table once and for all. This brilliant young scientist who died in World War I was in his twenties when he made his great contribution to science.

Another man, Niels Bohr, worked with Rutherford and was the first scientist to modify the Rutherford picture of the atom, making it more nearly conform to the experimental evidence of what atoms actually are. He answered the "self-destroying" question of Rutherford's model and went on to contribute to the World War II development of the atomic bomb.

Rutherford did not live to see the energy of the atomic nucleus put to use. But he knew it was there. From his study of radioactive materials he calculated it. As early as 1903, this experimental wizard in the realm of atoms made the statement in a speech before the British Association that ". . . it seems probable that the atomic energy of elements not yet found to be radioactive is of the same order of magnitude [as that of known radioactive elements] and may be set free by methods of which we are not yet cognisant."

Enrico Fermi: Architect of Nuclear Fission

Enrico Fermi was a member of the first generation of men to live in the atomic age. During his youth and early maturity there were no such terms as nuclear fission, fusion, chain reaction or neutron bombardment; in his middle and later years, those terms and the facts they represented not only existed but, in addition, they dominated the political thinking of the world. They still do.

No single experiment in the history of mankind illustrates more clearly the way by which scientific experiment and discovery have shaped our lives.

Before Fermi accomplished his work, both the eastern and western worlds pursued traditional aims of power and wealth by traditional means. Following Fermi's experiment, the traditional means of gaining power with armed force or the threat of force was no longer effective; indeed the entire idea of power by conquest became impractical because it was suicidal.

Enrico Fermi was one of the handful of scientists who successfully probed the secrets of the atom in the most exciting scientific search men have ever undertaken. Ironically, Fermi and many other scientists failed at first to realize the consequences of their work, failed actually to interpret the results correctly and so delayed the arrival of the atomic age by several years. He and others working on atomic structure were supremely intelligent men, trained in all the discipline of science, forewarned about interpretation of experimental results, and yet they missed seeing what actually was occurring in their experiments.

In 1938 Enrico Fermi received the Nobel prize in physics for his work on the nucleus of the atom. He had managed, by using neutrons which are uncharged nuclear particles, to transform the element uranium into other identifiable radioactive elements. Both his accomplishment and the methods he used were mentioned in the official Nobel citation.

What neither he nor other physicists knew then was that in his experiments he was within a hairsbreadth of discovering nuclear fission—the splitting of the atomic nucleus. As Fermi learned later, he actually was splitting the nuclei of uranium atoms in those early experiments, but by a curious circumstance the arrangement of his apparatus denied the knowledge of that fact to him. In addition to this, the most advanced physics theory of the day claimed that shattering the nuclei of atoms was not possible—so Fermi was not even looking for the occurrence.

Following Fermi's reception of the Nobel prize in Stockholm, Sweden, he and his family emigrated to the United States. He arrived early in January, 1939. Within less than a year the outstanding physicist was drawn into the dramatic and profoundly secret search for the method of releasing and utilizing atomic power.

In concert with other scientists he worked first at Columbia University and later at the University of Chicago in the attempt to produce the first controlled chain reaction of nuclear fission in history. In his great experiment performed beneath the empty football stadium of the University of Chicago, Fermi led mankind—for better or worse—into the age of nuclear power.

The need for secrecy and speed was apparent to everyone then. For the date of the experiment was December 2, 1942. Physicists knew that Nazi Germany was aware of the possibilities of nuclear fission and they assumed scientists in the Kaiser Wilhelm Institute in Berlin were working at top speed to harness the power of the atom to produce an atomic bomb. War, of course, had again interrupted the free exchange of scientific information and while no one knew for certain that the Germans were working rapidly, American scientists and government leaders had to assume they were—and act accordingly.

Enrico Fermi and his fellow physicists were in a race they had not chosen for a prize they did not want: the atomic bomb. The events of war had taken Fermi from the laboratory of pure research and placed him at a crucial point in the history of mankind. That point was the Squash Courts beneath the stadium of Stagg Field in Chicago where a curious cubical pile of graphite bricks rose above the concrete floor. Graphite dust covered the floor; voices echoed in the high-ceilinged room and when the leader of the research group, Enrico Fermi, gave the final order, the clicking of many Geiger counters grew louder and louder and louder. . . .

Enrico Fermi was born September 29, 1901, in Rome, Italy. His grandfather was the first of the family line to abandon farming, for the Fermis before that grandfather had been occupied by only one thing: earning a meager living on a small plot of ground as farmers. But Stefano Fermi, Enrico's grandfather, tried to break away from the tradition. He succeeded, but left little in the way of wealth to show for his life's work. Enrico's father, Alberto Fermi, was intelligent but not formally educated and he entered railroading as a career. He finally married at the age of forty-one and settled in Rome.

Like Edison and Newton before him, Enrico Fermi was not highly regarded as a student during his first years. He was small and unattractive and had the additional drawback of being untidy. His teachers believed he lacked imagination and any but the most ordinary intelligence. That it was the teachers who lacked those qualities was not suspected. He was shy with grownups and, perhaps because of his small size, aggressively talkative among children his own age.

In 1915 Enrico's older brother by a year, Guilio, died during an apparently minor operation, and that death affected Enrico profoundly. The two boys had been inseparable at work and at play. In Guilio, Enrico had a close friend as well as a brother and the loss desolated the young Fermi so much that he could not show his grief. He worked perfunctorily at school and played unenthusiastically at the boyhood games among his schoolmates and neighbors. To fill the lonely hours and stifle the grief he continued to feel, he began to study mathematics and physics outside of school. In his search for books on the subjects that interested him, he found a friend who, like himself, was searching for knowledge on his own. His name was Enrico Persico and he was interested in mathematics.

The two boys, still in high school, haunted the secondhand bookstores and devoured texts they found. They began to conduct their own experiments in physics.

A friend of Enrico's father, one Ingegner Almidei, noticed the young boy's enthusiasm for mathematics and science and jokingly at first, began giving him problems to solve which should have been far beyond Enrico's capacity. But Enrico solved them and asked for more. Almidei gave Enrico harder and harder problems and Enrico continued to solve them.

Finally he was solving problems that the older man could not solve.

Through Almidei, the now promising student of science obtained a scholarship to a small academy in Pisa, the Reale Scuola Normale Superiore, that accepted outstanding students in both the arts and sciences. When Enrico enrolled and began to attend classes that would fit him to become a physicist, he found that his own studying had placed him ahead of the curriculum. He did not have to study very hard to remain at the top of his class and he turned to having some fun as a student. Practical jokes and pranks played on other students and sometimes the innocent population of the town got Enrico into trouble more than once. But the exuberant young man was emerging, gifted, enthusiastic about life, and self-confident. The trait of self-confidence could be termed cockiness—except for the fact that it was well founded. His physics teacher let Enrico roam the laboratory as he wished and do any research that appealed to him. The older teacher had failed to keep abreast of the advances in his subject and before Enrico graduated, he was, at the teacher's request, giving him instruction in Einstein's relativity theory and other modern ideas in science.

At the age of 20 Enrico Fermi received his degree as Doctor of Physics, magna cum laude. His oral dissertation before the examining board put the members to sleep. They couldn't fathom what he was talking about so they quietly dozed until he had finished.

In 1926 Enrico Fermi settled in at the University of Rome as a full professor of physics. His reputation had grown following his graduation as he began to publish papers on the atom. He had studied and taught for brief intervals in Florence and in Germany but his return to Rome was due to the efforts of a patriotic Italian scientist, Orso Mario Corbino, who wanted to make Rome a center of scientific research that would attract the attention of the world. Enrico Fermi was his first "catch." Franco Rasetti, a former schoolmate of Fermi's, was Corbino's next find and the two friends formed the nucleus of a physics teaching and research group that was truly outstanding. Next to come was Emilio Segré, who transferred from an engineering course after great deliberation, graduated and joined the staff. Others followed, and Corbino's dream began to take shape. He had eager young men with great brains. He also had young men with a lot of life in them. Fermi and Rasetti engaged in horseplay and Segré joined in somewhat reluctantly. Segré never understood Fermi's love of games and contests—in which Fermi insisted on being first.

If a Sunday mountain climb was undertaken, Fermi bounded ahead of everyone to be first at the summit. If parlor games at a party were in order, Fermi argued and fought to win. He invented foolish games such as one which he called "fleas." Actually it was like tiddlywinks. He made pennies hop about on a living-room rug. Whatever the game, Fermi played to win.

Within a short time the three teachers, Fermi, Rasetti and Segré, gave themselves nicknames. Fermi became, irreverently, "The Pope," Rasetti "The Cardinal," and Segré "The Basilisk." Segré's name—that of a legendary serpent whose "breath and look were fatal"—came from his frequent loss of temper and angry glances at his two horseplaying colleagues.

This triumvirate was soon joined by two other young men of outstanding ability: Oscar D'Agostino and Edoardo Amaldi; but then the group suffered the loss of Rasetti who, though brilliantly equipped to be a physicist, also longed to be a biologist and went on distant journeys in search of moths and butterflies.

The group of young physicists carried their energy over into their laboratory work. By 1934 Fermi and his colleagues were bombarding elements with neutrons trying to produce artificial radioactivity. The neutron itself—an uncharged nuclear particle—was difficult to obtain as a "bullet" but Fermi produced a neutron source by using radon and berylium. The radon emitted Alpha particles which are positively charged. These in turn struck the berylium which was induced to emit neutrons. But the number of neutrons emitted was discouragingly small.

Fermi became interested in using neutrons because they have a great advantage over positively charged Alpha particles or even protons. Since each nucleus of an atom is positively charged itself, any positive particle like a proton that is aimed at atomic nuclei will be repelled by the positive nuclei. But neutrons, having no charge, can be directed at a sample of material and the "bullets" have a greater opportunity to strike and affect the positive nuclei. At first Fermi and his colleagues simply placed the neutron-emitting material near the sample under bombardment and let the neutrons proceed at whatever their speed was to strike the sample atoms. Later it was discovered that slowing the neutrons down (by passing them through water or paraffin) produced more hits on atomic nuclei than fast neutrons.

Fermi began his experiment with the lightest atom, hydrogen, and worked his way slowly through the entire list of elements, exposing each one in turn to neutron bombardment. Today such nuclear experiments are backed by ample funds from universities or the government. In Fermi's time the scientists had to build, beg, borrow or steal equipment and supplies. To get samples of as many elements as possible, Fermi sent Segré out to the markets around Rome with a shopping bag and handwritten list of materials to buy. Table salt, for instance,

could yield sodium and chlorine. Segré scoured the city phar-
macies for rarer elements while Fermi and Amaldi set to work.

Their method was physically simple: trap radon in a tube
immersed in liquid air so the radon, which is a gas at ordinary
temperatures, would condense to a liquid and not escape; seal
the tube of radon mixed with beryllium powder, and neutrons
will be emitted spontaneously.

After each element was exposed to the neutron bullets it was
checked for artificial radioactivity. To test each element to see
if it had become radioactive, they placed the irradiated sample
near Geiger counters. If the counters clicked abnormally, they
knew that the element had been made radioactive.

There was only one difficulty in the scheme. Since the neutron
source would make counters click rapidly too, the radon-
beryllium source was kept at one end of a hall and the counter
at the other. But more problems presented themselves: some
elements became radioactive for only a very short time, some
for as little as a minute or less—and the hall was long.

Fermi claimed he was the fastest runner. Amaldi disputed
him. They raced, laboratory coats flying out behind them, each
clutching a precious irradiated sample, to get to the Geiger
counters and check them. During one such unscientific contest,
a Spanish physicist came into the laboratory looking for the
famed physicist, Dr. Fermi. He was directed to the floor where
Fermi and Amaldi were having their foot races. The Spanish
visitor wandered about looking for the distinguished Dr. Fermi
but couldn't find him. In fact the only people he saw on the
floor were two odd fellows who tore out of one doorway and
ran down the hall to disappear into another office. Disconsolate,
the Spaniard returned to the floor below and was redirected to
the race track just as Fermi and Amaldi sped by again. His

guide pointed to one of the fleeing figures and identified him as the man in question.

Fermi worked his way through the entire group of 92 natural elements and many of them, he discovered, were made artificially radioactive by neutron bombardment. Uranium, the heaviest natural atom, was bombarded and one product of the bombardment was a substance which seemed to be an unknown element beyond uranium, element 93. Throughout his tests Fermi took precautions to protect himself and his instruments. Uranium is naturally radioactive and Fermi was bombarding it with neutrons. He knew that high energy radiation might result, so he placed a thin sheet of aluminum foil between the irradiated sample and the Geiger counters for protection. The foil was only three thousandths of an inch thick but it served its purpose far more efficiently than Fermi knew at the time. Had the aluminum foil not been in place Fermi, Amaldi and Segré would have been the first men in the world to witness atomic fission. For they were splitting uranium atoms. If that foil had been removed there would have been such a clamor from the Geiger counters they would have known something unusual was taking place. All three men were thoroughly grounded in theory and they could not have accounted for such amounts of energy being emitted without being led to the fact that the nuclei of uranium atoms were not simply capturing neutrons and emitting small particles. They would have known that the nucleus itself was being split into two comparably sized parts. In short, that the uranium atoms were fissioning. But with the aluminum foil in place the counters were shielded from the quantities of energy being produced.

Fermi's aim was to check degrees of induced radioactivity under neutron bombardment and learn how to use neutrons.

In these aims he was astonishingly successful. Soon scientists throughout Europe and the United States were duplicating his experiments—but always with the aluminum foil in place. In only one case was it omitted and then quite by accident. Two Swiss scientists were examining the action of neutron on uranium in 1936 and they forgot to place the foil between their recording instrument, the oscilloscope, and the sample. The oscilloscope, much like a television screen, could make the reception of emissions from the uranium visible. The indications these two scientists received were so large—going far off the screen—that they concluded there was something wrong with their electrical hookup. They disconnected the instrument and tried to locate the trouble. They did not know it at the time, but they were witnessing the phenomenon of nuclear fission.

Fermi's work with neutrons and artificial radioactivity led to his reception of the Nobel prize in 1938. At that time he knew as much about neutron bombardment and uranium as any man in the world. But there were many other scientists at work. Some of them in Nazi Germany; some in Sweden; some in Denmark, France, England and the United States.

As the fourth decade of the twentieth century ended, the world watched Adolf Hitler driving Europe closer to war. In Italy, Mussolini was tightening his grip on that nation and aligning himself more closely with Hitler. Fermi decided to emigrate to the United States. Immediately following his journey to Stockholm to receive the Nobel prize he set sail with his wife and family, arriving in New York City on January 2, 1939.

From the days of J. J. Thomson and the young Ernest Rutherford, physicists of the world searched, with growing excitement, for the secrets of the atom. New theories were formed on the very nature of matter; old theories had to be discarded or revised.

Rutherford and his colleagues worked on the atom with Alpha particles. In 1932 one of Rutherford's students, James Chadwick, discovered the existence of the neutron which had been predicted by Rutherford as far back as 1920. In France, Irène Joliot-Curie, daughter of Marie Curie, the discoverer of radium, was searching for the neutron at the same time. In Germany the team of Otto Hahn and Lise Meitner worked with a noted radiochemist, Fritz Strassman, trying to identify the growing assortment of "new elements" which resulted from Fermi's bombardment of the uranium atom with neutrons. The original work in this direction was based on the premise that an atomic nucleus would capture or absorb a neutron and emit one or more positive or negatively charged particles, thus transforming the original element into another one very close to it in weight and electrical charge. Until Fermi sent neutrons in the direction of uranium atoms, the products resulting from bombardment seemed to be nowhere near the uranium atom either in weight, charge or chemical characteristic.

As we know now—and as those early researchers were to find out very shortly—the products of neutron bombardment of uranium were fragments of the split nucleus. These fragments were known atoms but they were about half the weight of uranium nuclei. Researchers everywhere were splitting uranium atoms and did not know it.

Hitler's growing campaign against the Jews had an important effect on the development of science at this time. Lise Meitner, the veteran co-worker of Otto Hahn, was of Jewish descent. She had to abandon her work in Germany and flee—first to Holland and then to Copenhagen, where Rutherford's former pupil Niels Bohr had made the Institute for Theoretical Physics world-famous. After a visit there she went to Sweden and sought permanent refuge. Had Hitler allowed Miss Meitner to stay and work in the Kaiser Wilhelm Institute it is conceivable that Germany would have made more rapid strides in the looming struggle to unlock the energy of the atom, control it and produce the first atomic bomb. But neither Hitler nor other politicians and generals throughout the world knew or cared what the theoretical physicists were doing. They all faced a violent armed conflict and as war clouds gathered there seemed less and less excuse for men working to find out exactly what an atom was.

But by the time Fermi landed in New York, events—both political and scientific—were accelerating faster and faster, catching everyone up in the ominous momentum of the times.

Otto Hahn and Fritz Strassman continued their work in Berlin. Hahn kept in touch with Meitner in Sweden in a last desperate effort to maintain the communication lines among scientists. As 1938 ended, Hahn and Strassman, who were chemists, produced the first evidence of uranium fission. They were bombarding uranium with slow-moving neutrons and then analyzing the products after bombardment. The method was essentially chemical. The bombarded uranium was separated and analyzed by classical chemical methods. When they were through, both Hahn and Strassman were forced to the conclusion that what they had was no longer uranium but the elements barium, lanthanum and cerium.

Both men being chemists, not physicists, they were reluctant to state the now obvious truth that they had split the uranium atom. Physicists the world over still held that it was impossible. But they evidently had done just that.

Hahn wrote Meitner of the astonishing experiment and the results. He and Strassman prepared a paper on their work and arranged to have it published in January, 1939. Meitner pondered the meaning of the results and contacted Niels Bohr in Copenhagen. When Meitner explained what had happened in Berlin, Bohr reportedly slapped his forehead and exclaimed, "How could we have missed it all this time!"

Bohr left Denmark, journeyed to Sweden and then came to the United States for a visit with Einstein at the Institute for Advanced Studies at Princeton University. The trip had been planned in advance but the news Bohr brought with him was certainly not. Before he left Copenhagen, Bohr asked Otto Frisch, Lise Meitner's nephew, to check the Hahn-Strassman experiment. Bohr was in the United States when the news of Frisch's experiment came to him: there was no doubt that fission was taking place.

One of the things that drew the attention of physicists most strongly in the fission process was the enormous quantity of energy that was released. Physicists speak of such energies in terms of electron-volts which, if the terms are not understood, mean little to the layman. But press reports quickly translated the enormous source of energy into understandable terms: uranium fission has twenty-million times the explosive energy of TNT.

Essentially the experiments of Hahn-Strassman and Frisch were those of Fermi, with one important difference: the aluminum foil was not inserted between the uranium sample and the indicating instruments.

Fermi had barely settled in the United States when the news came. He had been offered a post at Columbia University and had met and begun to work with leading United States physicists. Bohr and Fermi at that time were among the leaders in modern physics and fate had placed both of them in the United States when the news of fission came. They were not the only

European physicists who had left their homelands. As Hitler's tyranny spread and war became inevitable, refugees from many affected countries came to England and the United States to carry on their work. All saw in uranium fission the possibility of a weapon of fantastic power. But they were physicists. Neither President Roosevelt nor any of his Cabinet or generals were aware of the importance of the discovery. At the urging of many of his colleagues the most famous refugee of them all, Albert Einstein, wrote his now historical letter to President Roosevelt.

In it, Einstein states that the probability of producing a controlled chain reaction with the use of slow neutrons was very good and that "This new phenomenon would lead to the construction of bombs, and it is conceivable—though much less certain—that extremely powerful bombs of a new type may thus be constructed. . . ."

Enrico Fermi and Leo Szilard duplicated the now famous experiment at Columbia University. The news spread like a conflagration in the formerly isolated world of the physicists.

As soon as the fact of fission was given him Fermi saw the possibility of a chain reaction. In effect, the chain reaction relies on the release of neutrons by the material being broken up, the uranium. If one neutron from the radon-beryllium source splits a uranium atom, two neutrons are released. These in turn split two uranium atoms and four neutrons are released. The four release eight; the eight, sixteen, and so on. Beyond a certain point, theory and mathematics indicated, the radon-beryllium source could be removed and the reaction would continue— it would be, as physicists say, self-sustaining. If the reaction is not controlled, however, the number of neutrons increases at a fantastic rate; if sufficient uranium is present and the energy of all the fissioned atoms is expended within a millionth of a second, an atomic explosion results.

Suddenly Fermi and the other physicists found themselves the object of much interest and attention from the government. Hitler had invaded Poland. England and France had declared war. Newsreels in the United States showed the advancing German divisions, and sound tracks shrieked with the wail of Stuka dive bombers as Poland was obliterated.

Fermi, technically an enemy alien when Italy joined Germany in war, found himself shuttling back and forth between Columbia and the University of Chicago as plans to try to produce a sustained controlled chain reaction took shape. Of all the physicists in the world, he had the longest experience in the laboratory with neutron bombardment. But it was no longer a race from one end of a laboratory hall to the other; it was a race to save the world from German conquest. All anyone knew certainly about German research was that Hahn and Strassman remained in Berlin. All shipments of uranium ore from the mines in Czechoslovakia were marked for Berlin. More and more physicists gathered at the Kaiser Wilhelm Institute. Fermi and others had to conclude that German research was ahead of their own.

Months dragged by and the government officials in Washington paid little attention to the problem of uranium fission. To many of them it all seemed so remote, so unlikely to produce quick results, that they turned their attention to other matters. Fermi fretted. Bohr and Compton and Szilard and many other physicists could get no action. A few thousand dollars had been allocated for research but it was nowhere near what was needed to do the job.

Then a scientist from England, Dr. Oliphant, came to Washington. He told the government that England was pushing ahead on research into atomic fission and that her scientists would share all their knowledge if we would join them in what they knew to be a race.

While the government was undecided, Fermi began experimental work at Columbia University. Bohr and his colleague Dr. Wheeler had found a theoretical solution to one of the most vexing problems connected with the production of a chain reaction.

The problem was this. Uranium is made up of two forms: one has a weight of 238, the other has a weight of 235 atomic mass units. U_{235}, as the lighter isotope is called, would fission when struck with neutrons. U_{238} would absorb neutrons and stop the reaction. Since U_{238} made up about 99 per cent of natural uranium ores, it seemed unlikely that a sustained reaction could be produced. In addition, at that time there was no known method of separating U_{235} from U_{238}. But Niels Bohr calculated that U_{238} absorbed or "captured" fast neutrons more readily than slow ones. Slow neutrons actually were drawn to the fissionable U_{235} atoms and by-passed the others. If his calculations were correct, the chain reaction could be produced by using slow neutrons: those traveling on the order of a mile per second rather than ten thousand miles per second. Fortunately, Fermi knew as much as anyone about how to slow down neutrons. He set to work at first at Columbia University and later, when the government overcame its inertia, at the famous location beneath the football stands at Stagg Field in Chicago.

By today's standards, Fermi's method and apparatus were both crude and simple. To slow down his neutrons he planned to let them travel through carbon in the form of graphite bricks. The fissionable material was to be as much pure uranium as he could get plus uranium oxide, which would contain both

U_{235} and U_{238}. But he needed much more than a test tube full of both materials. One of the critical factors in the experiment was sufficient uranium to produce enough neutrons. With the calculated quantity of uranium he also needed a large quantity of graphite bricks. The apparatus, of bricks and uranium, was going to form a sizable pile.

The principal reason the Squash Courts at the University of Chicago were chosen was because they had a twenty-six foot high ceiling. Fermi could stack bricks to his heart's content there.

One other factor had to be taken into account in building the world's first atomic pile or reactor: a control mechanism in case there was a runaway reaction. To lessen or stop the fission of atoms and the production of more neutrons, the obvious way was to soak up neutrons with some sort of blotter. For if the neutrons were not allowed to enter the U_{235} atoms, the reaction would stop. Fermi knew that the elements boron and cadmium absorbed neutrons, so he planned to use cadmium rods to insert into the pile of graphite and uranium. The inserted rods would absorb neutrons and "put out the fire." The rods, however, could be withdrawn in varying amounts and so speed up or slow down the reaction.

As Fermi assembled his materials and arranged his recording instruments, 1942 was drawing to a close. The United States was deeply involved in a two-front war. The capacity of the nation was being strained to the limit to produce the arms and the armies to fight the Japanese across the wide Pacific Ocean and the Germans on the other side of the world.

The government decided to push forward as fast as possible to develop an atomic bomb. Secrecy was most important, and Fermi and his co-workers figuratively vanished behind the screen of a top-secret classification. Enrico Fermi and others who had begun examining the possibilities of a chain reaction earlier had decided among themselves that secrecy was important, but now, with millions of dollars and enormous quantities of men and materials involved, the problem of security was even more apparent and difficult to solve. When Fermi first went to the University of Chicago he and the other physicists conferred and experimented in the Metallurgical Laboratory. They became—so far as the outside world knew—metallurgists, although there was not a single metallurgist in the building as they worked. The entire effort was termed the Manhattan Project and it extended far beyond Fermi and his particular experiment.

Ordinarily in a vast enterprise of this kind, years of patient research and production testing precede the development of the final product. But the United States and its Allies did not have the time to spend on the usual methods. As Fermi was constructing his gigantic experimental pile, administrators of the project actually were consulting with men from industry to discuss their building of a production pile. Top men of E. I. Du Pont Co. had been approached and the men who talked with the company representative had to admit that they were talking of something which had not yet been proved workable.

For although all theory and preliminary experiments pointed to the success of the pile Fermi was building, actual experiment had not confirmed it. The physicists, chemists and engineers who had been drawn into the project were not relying entirely on the graphite-uranium pile as a solution. They knew that U_{235} was the fissionable material and that if they could separate it in quantity they could produce a chain reaction or a bomb. The problem could not be solved by ordinary chemical analysis, for both U_{235} and U_{238} had identical reactions to chemical treatments.

Physicist Ernest O. Lawrence at the University of California moved ahead with his idea of separation using a mass spectrograph method. At first he was only capable of separating a few millionths of a gram of the material.

The idea of using centrifuges was discussed and tried. These machines acted like cream separators and since the two forms of uranium had different masses, they should be separable by this method. But the practical problems of building a centrifuge that would attain the required high speeds and remain stable were formidable. The other method of separation—and the one eventually used in the Oak Ridge, Tennessee, plant—was a method called gaseous diffusion. In vapor form, the two isotopes of uranium would diffuse or filter through especially designed barriers at different rates of speed that were dependent on their mass difference. The lighter form, U_{235}, went through the filter faster. If it could be collected on the low pressure side of the filter, and refined again and again, it was believed U_{235} could be obtained in sufficient quantity to produce an atomic bomb. England had decided on this method of separation before the United States reached a decision, and English physicists had calculated that 10 kilograms (approximately 22 pounds) of pure U_{235} would be enough to produce an atomic explosion.

Yet not all efforts were concentrated on U_{235}. In Berkeley, California, Lawrence and Emile Segré, Fermi's colleague from Rome, had produced and positively identified elements 93 and 94. Element 93 they named Neptunium—for the planet in our solar system next beyond Uranus, after which uranium (92) had been named. Element 94 became Plutonium, a namesake of our outermost planet. Plutonium, physicists agreed, could be made to fission even more spectacularly than U_{235}. So projects began to produce plutonium as well as purify uranium. But in order to produce plutonium, a controlled chain reaction had to supply neutrons.

By December 2, 1942, Fermi had his experimental apparatus ready. The graphite-uranium pile on the floor of the Squash Court contained six tons of pure uranium metal, 50 tons of uranium oxide and 400 tons of pure graphite. The uranium was spaced throughout the rectangular structure with graphite bricks in between to slow the neutrons when they were produced. Control rods of cadmium pierced the entire, monstrous structure. Geiger counters connected to control panels were in their places. The neutron source of radon and berylium was in place. All Fermi had to do to start the experiment was to direct the workers to withdraw the cadmium rods.

Fermi, the other physicists, and one skeptical representative from the Du Pont company gathered on a platform overlooking the pile. Three young workers stood on scaffolding above the pile with buckets of cadmium solution, as a precautionary measure. They were known, half-seriously and half-jokingly, as the "suicide squad." For despite all calculation, all theory, there was fear of the unknown forces which Fermi was about to let loose. The reaction should be controllable; but was it? Suppose some unknown factor operated in a pile this size to make the controlled reaction uncontrollable? The three young men with their buckets represented the last safety valve. No one knew whether they would be necessary or not.

Fermi told his waiting, listening audience of scientists and engineers that a single cadmium rod should be sufficient to prevent the chain reaction. He then ordered that all rods but one be removed from the pile. An assistant, George Weill, remained on the floor of the Squash Court to remove the last cadmium rod on command. He looked lonely standing by himself beside the huge pile.

Fermi assured everyone that that last rod was automatically controlled and that should a runaway reaction begin, it would be drawn back into the pile by a mechanism linked to the clicking Geiger counters. But he still felt the three men with buckets of solution should stay in place.

Fermi appeared tired but confident as he called to Weill to draw the last cadmium rod out a short distance. As the rod slid out, the Geiger counters began to click more rapidly. A pen on an automatic recording graph drew a line upward showing the increase in radiation—then it leveled off. The reaction was under control.

The Du Pont representative being initiated into the mysteries of modern physics was most visibly impressed. He had been told of uranium fission, slow neutrons, chain reactions and all the rest. But he could scarcely be expected to believe everything without question. Whatever questions he may have had were being answered before his eyes.

Foot by foot the rod was drawn out. Each time it moved out a little farther the pen on the graph rose a little higher—just as Fermi predicted it would.

At 3:20 P.M. on the afternoon of December 2, 1942, Fermi told George Weill to pull the cadmium rod out one more foot. Then he turned to the group and said, "The reaction will be self-sustaining now."

With the rod withdrawn that last critical distance, enough neutrons were free to produce controlled fission. The pen on the graph rose steadily higher and higher and higher. . . .

Man had learned how to release and control the energy locked within the atom.

The man from Du Pont was enthusiastic. He was ready to agree that whatever was going on before his eyes, he wanted his company to be part of it.

Following that historic moment, Dr. Arthur Compton, head of the Chicago phase of uranium research, called Dr. James Conant at Harvard in Cambridge, Massachusetts, to give him the news of success. Both men knew the need for secrecy and so they had agreed upon a code.

Dr. Compton said, "Jim, this is Arthur. I thought you would want to know that the Italian Navigator has landed in the new world."

Dr. Conant said, "What? Already?"

Dr. Compton said, "Yes, the earth was smaller than estimated and he arrived several days earlier than he expected."

Dr. Conant asked, "Were the natives friendly?"

Dr. Compton said, "They were indeed. Everyone landed safe and happy."

It was indeed a new world. A world that none of the men working then could actually define. Under the pressure of war, work went forward at an accelerated pace. The scientists— Fermi among them—eventually trekked westward to an unknown place in the desert called Alamogordo, New Mexico. Great production plants to produce U_{235} and plutonium rose in Tennessee and Washington.

On August 6, 1945, a lone B-29, the *Enola Gay,* dropped a single bomb over Hiroshima, Japan, at 8:15 Hiroshima time and an estimated 100,000 people died.

The world, indeed, had been shaped anew by science.

About the Author

William Bixby was born in San Diego, California, of a Navy family and grew up in California, Florida, and Tennessee where he attended public schools. He took an engineering degree in college and upon graduation in 1942 entered the Service. He served first as a Signal Corps Officer and later transferred to the Air Corps. He served as a pilot with the 8th Air Force in England. In 1945 he took up a career in journalism and for eight years was a magazine writer and associate editor on a number of New York publications.

In 1953 he decided to leave the city to teach and work on his own books. He settled in New England, where his family originated, and has taught variously in public and private schools in Vermont, Massachusetts, and Rhode Island. Presently he is a part-time instructor of physics at New Haven College, New Haven, Connecticut. Mr. Bixby is married and has two children: a son, William Jr., and a daughter, Barbara.

Mr. Bixby's books are: *Havoc, the Story of Natural Disasters; McMurdo, Antarctica; The Race to the South Pole; Skywatchers, the U.S. Weather Bureau in Action; Waves, Pathways of Energy,* and now *Great Experimenters.*

Index